Efficient Electric Motor Systems Handbook

Efficient Electric Motor Systems Handbook

Todd Litman

Published by
THE FAIRMONT PRESS, INC.
700 Indian Trail
Lilburn, GA 30247

Library of Congress Cataloging-in-Publication Data

Litman, Todd.
   Efficient electric motor systems handbook by Todd Litman.
   p. cm.
   ISBN 0-88173-197-8
   1. Electric motors--Handbooks, manuals, etc. 2. Electric
driving--Handbooks, manuals, etc. I. Title.
TK2511.L54   1995   621.46--dc20   94-43747
                                                CIP

Published by The Fairmont Press, Inc.
700 Indian Trail
Lilburn, GA 30247

Printed in the United States of America

10 9 8 7 6 5 4 3 2 1

ISBN 0-88173-197-8   FP

ISBN 0-13-378134-8   PH

While every effort is made to provide dependable information, the publisher, authors, and
editors cannot be held responsible for any errors or omissions.

Distributed by Prentice Hall PTR
Prentice-Hall, Inc.
A Simon & Schuster Company
Englewood Cliffs, NJ 07632

Prentice-Hall International (UK) Limited, London
Prentice-Hall of Australia Pty. Limited, Sydney
Prentice-Hall Canada Inc., Toronto
Prentice-Hall Hispanoamericana, S.A., Mexico
Prentice-Hall of India Private Limited, New Delhi
Prentice-Hall of Japan, Inc., Tokyo
Simon & Schuster Asia Pte. Ltd., Singapore
Editora Prentice-Hall do Brasil, Ltda., Rio de Janeiro

DEDICATION

To Byron Youtz, 1925 – 1992, whose enthusiasm for physics and commitment to use knowledge for the betterment of humanity inspired generations of students. This book is a legacy of his generous guidance and friendship.

Table of Contents

Preface ix

Chapter 1
Introduction 1

Chapter 2
Types of Motors..7

Chapter 3
Efficiency 21

Chapter 4
Performance Characteristics...41

Chapter 5
Electric Power Supply 59

Chapter 6
Operating Characteristics...73

Chapter 7
Energy Efficient Motors 85

Chapter 8
Motor Controls 107

Chapter 9
Motor Repairs...121

Chapter 10
Predictive and Preventive Maintenance 137

Chapter 11
Investment Analysis 161

Chapter 12
Selecting Motors 183

Chapter 13
Putting Together Your Motor System Optimization Program 209

Appendices:

A. Motor Nameplate and Catalog Glossary 217

B. Lincoln Motors Troubleshooting Charts 227

C. Motor Purchase Specification Form 231

D. Motor Inventory and Test Form 233

E. Motor Repair Shop Evaluation Forms 235

F. Electric Motor Repair Specifications...........................257

G. Motor Repair Form 297

H. Motor Repairer's Quality Record 299

I. Resources (i. Organizations; ii. Documents; iii. Software;
    iv. Standards) 305

Index 319

Preface

Electric motors are among modern technology's most useful and versatile tools. You probably rely on several each day to pump your water, circulate your air, keep your food cool, and eliminate drudgery. They provide essential services in virtually all commercial and industrial facilities.

Induction motors are efficient and reliable when properly used, but many factors in motor system design and operation can waste energy and cause premature failures. Because of their tremendous economic and energy importance it is essential to optimize motor systems for efficiency and reliability. The **Efficient Electric Motor Systems Handbook** provides comprehensive and easy to understand information on this subject.

Motors themselves are just one component of an electric drive system, which includes the power supply, control and protection devices, operating environment, transmission system and driven equipment. It is therefore important that equipment designers and operators become familiar with both general concepts and specific issues for optimizing total motor systems. An understanding of motor operating conditions, electrical power quality, motor control strategies, and preventive maintenance is critical for anybody working with motors.

The **Efficient Electric Motor Systems Handbook** can help engineers and operators in industrial, commercial, municipal and agricultural sectors increase efficiency, save energy and improve reliability. It incorporates current knowledge on electric motor equipment selection, operation, motor controls, electrical power supply, predictive and preventive maintenance, and economics. This book takes a systems approach. It suggests a step-by-step program to help you make the various parts of your drive system work together to improve efficiency, avoid failures and provide the most effective process control.

The first chapters of this book lay a foundation for understanding motor systems and the opportunities for improving efficiency and reliability. With this foundation you can use the practices recommended in later chapters to develop a systems approach to motor drive improvements that is specific to your situation. This book focuses on three phase induction motors since they are the "workhorse" of the motor world, consuming the majority of electricity used by motors.

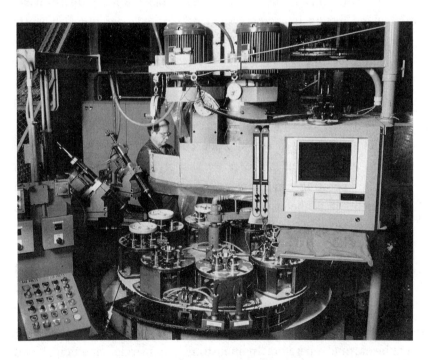

Figure 1-0 Electric motors are used in nearly every industry.
(Courtesy of Lincoln Electric)

ACKNOWLEDGEMENTS

Richard Been; Steve Darby; Johnny Douglass; Robert Gray; Robert K. Hoshide; Ziba Kellum; Rob Knapp; Gil McCoy; Karen Meadows; Dick Nailen; Rob Penney; Tom Ristow; Melba Slaughter; Wayne Stebbins; Jonathan Stine; Darryl Van Son; Dan Threlkel; Craig Wohlgemuth; and all of my colleagues at the Washington State Energy Office.

And to Suzanne, Graham, and Raviv for their support.

Chapter 1

Introduction

The universe is busy spinning, twirling and rotating. Winds circle around the earth, which spins on its axes, and circles around the sun, which rotates with billions of other stars around our galaxy. Countless human artifacts also employ rotation. Toys, clockworks, vehicles, mills, and other appliances rely on a circulating motion. There are many sources of rotating power. Hand cranks and treadmills operate simple tools. Water and wind have turned mills and pumps for centuries. But work done by these methods is constrained by the limitations of these power sources and must be located where they are available. A breakthrough occurred in the late 19th Century with the development of generators that convert rotating power into electricity, and electric motors that convert electricity back into rotating power. This extremely flexible and reliable way to deliver power resulted in the myriad variations of motor drive applications that we now enjoy.

Electric motors drive all types of machinery, from residential refrigerators to automobile assembly line conveyors. Electric motor powered pumps and fans supply water to your faucet as well as the air you breathe in mechanically ventilated buildings. Electric motor powered operations dominate many industries. Nearly every industrial process relies on electric motors for at least one critical function.

Figure 1-1   Estimated Portion of Total U.S. Electricity Used by Motors

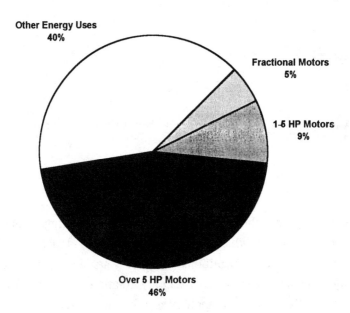

Industrial size motors use the largest portion of electrical energy, representing almost half of all electricity consumption in the U.S.

There are an estimated one billion stationary motors in use in the United States. Most of these, such as the single phase motors in household appliances and tools, are relatively small and operate only occasionally. Three-phase induction motors drive heavier applications such as large pumps, fans, and industrial process equipment. Because they consume considerable amounts of electricity and tend to operate long hours, three phase motors use the largest share of energy, accounting for almost half of all electricity consumed.

Induction motors are efficient and reliable when properly used, but many factors in motor system design and operation can cause energy waste and equipment downtime. Many of these problems can be avoided with a little planning and preventive maintenance. Motors are often ignored until they fail. Then they become the center of attention. This results in motors being purchased on a crisis basis, when the most important concern is quick delivery and a low purchase price rather than minimizing long-term costs. Energy costs are often ignored because they are "somebody else's problem." This book describes how to develop a better approach to motor system operation.

Each motor application is unique. You must consider a variety of factors when selecting a motor to obtain one that operates efficiently and reliably under its operating conditions. Optimizing each motor system can save energy and reduce failures. There is, however, no single way to accomplish this. Rather, there are many small steps that must be taken to avoid common problems.

An electric motor drive system includes the electrical supply, controls, the motor, the mechanical transmission system and the driven equipment (Figure 1-2). It is impossible to improve a system's overall efficiency without an understanding of the way these interact. Some steps that increase the efficiency of individual components can actually backfire, reducing the system's overall efficiency. Fortunately, you can avoid these problems with good information and careful planning.

Figure 1-2   Motor Drive System

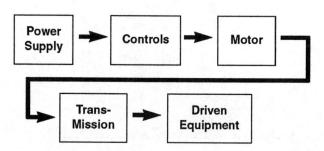

Each part of the motor drive system affects overall efficiency and reliability.

PURCHASE PRICE VERSUS OPERATING COSTS

What does a motor cost? A few hundred dollars? A couple thousand dollars? The real cost of a motor is much more than what you pay to buy it. Operating costs greatly exceed most motor's purchase price. For example, a standard 50 horsepower 91.7% efficient motor that costs $1,620 to buy new and operates 8,000 hours a year at 3/4 load uses 244,057 kWh annually. At 5¢ per kWh this is worth $12,203 per year, or 7.5 times its purchase price. Over a typical 15 year operating life it will consume over 100 times its purchase price worth of electricity.

An energy efficient 50 horsepower motor typically costs about $1,875, or $255 more than the standard model, and is 3 percentage points more efficient. Operating under the conditions described above it consumes 236,325 kWh each year, worth $11,816, for an annual savings of $387 compared with the standard motor. This energy efficient motor repays its price premium in less than 9 months!

Figure 1-3   Motor Purchase Price Compared with Annual Energy Costs

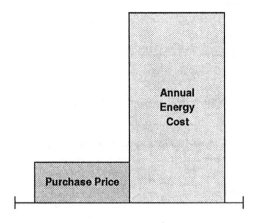

Induction motors typically use several times their purchase price worth of electricity each year.

To put the potential benefit of improved motor efficiency into perspective, let's compare these energy savings against automobile fuel costs. Based on 12,000 miles driven each year, a fuel efficiency of 24 miles per gallon, and gasoline costing $1.50 per gallon, the annual fuel cost of a typical car is $720, only about 5% of a $15,000 purchase price. A 25% improvement in fuel efficiency (to 33 mpg) saves 116 gallons per year, worth $175. This is less than half the savings offered by an energy efficient motor. Because of the tremendous amount of energy that three phase motors consume, a small improvement of just 3 points in efficiency rating actually saves more money than a 25% improvement in automobile fuel efficiency.

Table 1-1   Comparing Automobile and 50-horsepower
Electric Motor Costs

	Standard Automobile	Efficient Automobile	Standard Motor	Efficient Motor
Purchase Price	$15,000	$16,000	$1,620	$1,875
Price Premium	$0	$1,000	$0	$255
Annual Use	12,000 miles	12,000 miles	8,000 hours	8,000 hours
Efficiency	24 MPG	32 MPG	91.7%	94.7%
Unit Energy Cost	$1.50/gal	$1.50/gal	$0.05/kWh	$0.05/kWh
Annual Energy Cost	$750	$562	$12,203	$11,816
Annual Energy Cost Vs. Purchase Price	5%	3.5%	753%	630%
Annual Savings of Efficient Option		$188		$387
Annual Savings as Percent of Price Premium		19%		152%

The cost of energy as a portion of purchase price is much higher for a motor than for an automobile. Since motors often last for over a decade, the lifetime savings of an energy efficient model is usually many times greater than the price premium.

Of course it is important to consider motor reliability as well as efficiency. In many situations the cost of a motor failure in terms of lost production and replacement expenses is far greater than the financial value of the electricity saved by an energy efficient motor, as shown in Table 1-2.

Table 1-2   Estimated Production Downtime Costs for Selected Industries

Forest Industries	$10,000/hour
Food Processing	$40,000/hour
Petroleum and Chemical	$100,000/hour
Metal Casting	$125,000/hour
Automotive	$250,000/hour

The importance of reliability should not diminish your efforts to improve motor system efficiency. Steps to improve efficiency by installing new equipment, addressing power quality problems, increased testing and preventive maintenance also increase reliability. Motor system energy losses become heat, which cause deterioration of insulation, lubrication and other critical components. Energy efficient motors produce less heat and tend to incorporate higher quality materials that are more durable. Many manufacturers offer longer warrantees for energy efficient models. For these reasons, mechanics, operation engineers, and facility managers should implement energy management programs and purchase energy efficient equipment despite the extra initial cost.

Chapter 2

Types of Motors

ELECTRIC MOTOR CLASSIFICATIONS

Direct Current (DC)

Until recently, work requiring speed adjustments made DC motors the popular choice. Recent improvements in AC adjustable speed controls, however, now allow AC motors to replace DC motors in many applications. DC motors are still used where batteries or other DC power is available. They are often used to power vehicles, including subways and diesel-electric locomotives, in which case they are called "traction" motors. When powered from the AC electrical grid, DC motors require a power converter and have relatively high maintenance requirements, resulting in higher operating costs than an AC induction motor.

Single-phase AC

These are the most common type of fractional (less than one horsepower) motor and are available in sizes up to 10 hp. There are several common designs based on starting and wiring configuration. Single-phase motors are inherently less efficient than three-phase motors and require extra starting components, making them less

Figure 2-0   "Sea of Motors"
(Courtesy of Leeson Electric Corporation)

desirable where three-phase power is available, especially in larger size applications. Although fractional single-phase motors are extremely common, representing about 90% of all stationary motors, they use less than 10-percent of the total energy used by motors, due to their relatively small loads and low hours of operation.

Three-phase Synchronous

Synchronous motors are more complex and expensive than a comparable induction motor because they require special starting windings. These motors are occasionally used for large load, low speed operations. Unlike induction motors, synchronous motors always turn at exactly the same speed as the stator's rotating electric field. Because they produce a leading power factor (as described in Chapter 5), synchronous motors can be used for power factor correction.

Three-phase Induction

This class of motor receives its name from the fact that its rotors are energized by an *induced* voltage, rather than a direct electrical connection, making them relatively inexpensive to produce and operate. There are two main types of induction motors:

Wound Rotor

The rotor of this type of motor is wound with wire coils, which
are is relatively expensive to produce and repair. This gives motor
designers great control of the motor's performance characteristics, so
they are sometimes used when special torque and acceleration per-

Figure 2-1 Types of Electric Motors

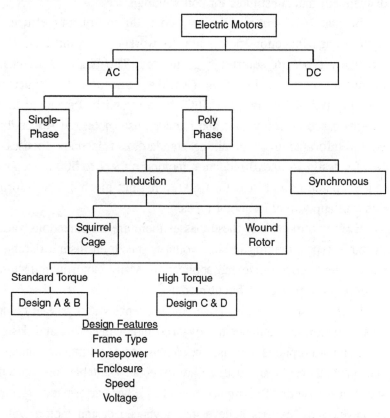

There are many types of electric motors. NEMA design A and B squirrel cage three-phase induction motors are the most common for heavy industrial applications that operate long hours, and therefore consume the majority of electricity used to operate motors. These motors offer many opportunities for low cost energy savings.

formance is required, and for adjustable speed applications. Wound rotor motors represent a small portion of the integral (one horsepower or larger) motor population.

Squirrel Cage

These are the most common type of integral motors, and are the primary focus of this book. Squirrel cage induction motors are the simplest and by far the most common type of three-phase motor. They are called "squirrel cage" motors due to the shape of the rotor bar structure (which cannot be seen unless the motor is completely dismantled) that substitutes for coil windings.

Because of their relative low cost, durability and efficiency, squirrel cage induction motors are the workhorse of industry. There are many types of squirrel cage motors. The National Electrical Manufacturers Association (NEMA) and the International Electrotechnical Commission (IEC) have established standard motor designs based on frame size and intended use (note: see Appendix I-vi. for information on obtaining standards). This book focuses on NEMA design A and B induction motors in the 1 to 500 horsepower range, operating with less than 600 Volts, but much of the information will apply to other motor types.

Even within each of these classes there are a tremendous variety of motor types, ranging in size, voltage, speed, enclosure, durability, performance, price range and application. Many motor manufacturers produce thousands of different models.

Research sponsored by government agencies and private companies is exploring a number of advanced motor materials and designs, including amorphous metals, superconductors, permanent magnets, and many more. Some of these are especially suitable for adjustable speed drive use or offer greater control of other performance features. However, most experts believe that advanced design motors will be relatively expensive and limited in use for the foreseeable future.

HOW INDUCTION MOTORS WORK

A motor's stationary frame, called the *stator,* is slotted to provide room for copper electrical wires, called windings. These are insulated and formed in coils within the slots. Most motors of 200 horsepower or less are *random wound,* which means that the coils are made of small wires bundled together. Larger, higher voltage motors are often *form wound,* which means that rectangular cross section windings are machine formed into the required shape and then wrapped with extra insulation before being fitted into the stator slots. When an electrical current is applied to these windings a rotating magnetic field is created that progresses around the stator. This rotating field spins at the speed determined by the line frequency (60 cycles per second in North America) and the number of *poles* (windings) in the stator. This is called the *synchronous* speed of the motor, which is usually 900, 1200, 1800 or 3600 RPM.

Fitted in the space within the stator and supported by bearings at each end is the *rotor.* The rotor of an induction motor has internal bars that resemble a squirrel cage, from which it gets its common name. As the rotating magnetic field sweeps past the rotor it induces a voltage that results in circulating currents within these bars. Because this current is induced without a direct electrical connection to the rotor by brushes or slip rings, these are called *induction* motors. These currents, in turn, set up their own revolving magnetic fields. The rotor magnetic fields are simultaneously pulled and pushed by the moving stator fields, creating a rotating force, or torque, which accelerates the rotor. The greater the difference in speed between the rotor and stator fields, the more current the stator windings draw and the more torque the motor produces. As the speed of the rotor approaches the motor's synchronous speed, the current in the rotor decreases, reducing the torque on the rotor. The rotor can never quite catch up to the rotation speed of the stator's field. As a load is applied to the rotor its speed decreases, increasing the current flow in the rotor and the torque. Thus, the motor maintains an equilibrium between energy consumption, torque, speed and load.

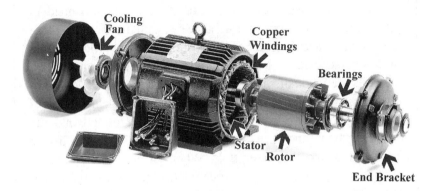

This illustration shows the major components of a three-phase, squirrel cage induction motor, which are the focus of this book. These motors are simple, reliable and relatively inexpensive. They are also relatively efficient, typically converting 85-95% of input electrical energy into useful mechanical power. Squirrel cage induction motors are the workhorse of industrial and commercial drive power, use the greatest portion of electricity, and offer the greatest potential for energy savings of all types of motors. (Courtesy of Leeson Electric Corporation)

DESIGN

NEMA has established four standard motor designs, based on various performance features, as shown in Table 2-1.

Design A and B motors are similar except that design B inrush current is limited to a specified maximum (which varies from 500% to 800% of operating current, depending on rating) while design A is unrestricted. NEMA design A and B motors are suitable for applications with medium or low locked-rotor torque requirements, including pumps, fans and production equipment with relatively constant loads. Design B is the most common type of induction motor, representing over 80% of all squirrel cage motors.

Design C and D motors have relatively high locked-rotor torque, making them suitable for applications such as conveyers, cranes, fixed displacement compressors, process equipment and machine tools with fluctuating loads. Locked-rotor torque is a major performance consideration in these applications. NEMA design A and B motors are inherently more efficient under constant loads, but design D motors are more efficient during acceleration, and so may be more efficient overall for applications that involve constant load variation.

Table 2-1   Motor Design Torque, Current and Slip Characteristics

NEMA Design	Starting Current	Locked-Rotor Torque	Breakdown Torque	Percent Slip	Applications
A	High	Variable	High	Low	Low or moderate starting inertia, constant speed loads. Fans, blowers, rotary pumps, and light conveyors and machine tools.
B	Medium	Medium	High	Medium	Same as design A
C	Medium	High	Medium	High	High starting inertia, constant speed loads. Crusher drums, fly wheels, heavy conveyors, piston pumps and compressors
D	Medium	Highest	Low	Highest	Very high starting inertia, variable speed loads. Cranes, hoists, elevators, machine tools.

The four design classifications established by NEMA allow users to easily identify motors that are suitable for common applications. Some motors are designed for a specific use and do not meet any of these design standards.

FRAME

NEMA frame specifications define the external physical dimensions of induction motors. Most North American induction motors under 500 horsepower are designed to a standard NEMA frame size. The IEC produces another set of motor design standards based on metric units that are widely used in other parts of the world. These

Figure 2-3 NEMA Frame Dimensions (inches)

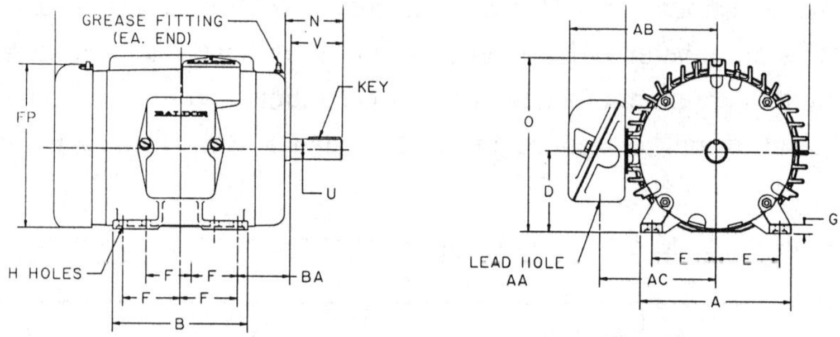

NEMA FRAME	FOOT MOUNTING BA	E	F	G	H	SHAFT DIMENSION N	U	V	KEY	CONDUIT BOX AA	AB	AC	FRAME A	B	C	D	O	P	FP	BEARINGS ODE	DE
143T	1 23/32	2 3/4	2	5/32	11/32	2 1/2	7/8	2 1/4	3/16	1 1/16	6 5/8	5	6 1/2	5 7/8	12 9/16	3 1/2	7 31/64	6 5/8	6 5/8	203	205
145T			2 1/2																		
182T	2 3/4	3 3/4	2 1/4	1/2	13/32	2 13/16	1 1/8	2 3/4	1/4	1 1/16	7 1/8	5 3/4	8 5/8	6 1/2	16 1/16	4 1/2	9 1/4	10 1/8	10 1/8	205	206
184T			2 3/4												16 1/8						
213T	3 1/2	4 1/4	2 3/4	5/8	13/32	3 3/8	1 3/8	3 3/8	5/16	1 1/16	8 11/16	7 3/16	9 1/2	8	17 15/16	5 1/4	10 1/16	12 5/16	12 5/16	206	307
215T			3 1/2												19 1/16						
254U 256U	4 1/4	5	4 1/8 5	13/16	17/32	4 1/16	1 3/8	3 3/4	5/16	1 3/8	9 1/2	8	11 1/2	11 1/2	22 13/16	6 1/4	12 7/8	12 15/16	13 1/4	208	309
254T 256T			4 1/8 5			4 5/16	1 5/8	4	3/8						23 5/16						
284U 286U	4 3/4	5 1/2	4 3/4 5 1/2	7/8	17/32	5	1 5/8	4 7/8	3/8	2	12 5/8	10	12 3/4	12 3/4	27 13/16	7	15 5/16	14 5/8	15	309	311
284T 286T			4 3/4 5 1/2			4 3/4	4 5/8	1 7/8	1/2						27 37/64						
324U 326U	5 1/4	6 1/4	5 1/4 6	1	21/32	5 13/16	1 7/8	5 5/8	1/2	2	14 1/8	11 5/16	14 1/2	14	30 5/8	8	16 1/2	17 3/8	16 15/16	311	312
324T 326T			5 1/4 6			5 7/16	2 1/8	5 1/4							30 1/4						
364U 365U	5 7/8	7	5 5/8 6 1/8	1	21/32	6 3/8	2 1/8	6 3/8	1/2	2	15 1/16	12 7/16	16 1/2	13 1/2 14 1/2	32 1/16 33 1/16	9	18 1/2	18 7/8	19	312	313
364T 365T			5 5/8 6 1/8			6 1/8	2 3/8	5 7/8	5/8	2 1/2				14 1/2	31 5/16 32 5/16						
404U 405U	6 5/8	8	6 1/8 6 7/8	1 1/8	13/16	7 3/8	2 3/8	7 1/8	5/8	3	18	14 7/16	18 3/4	15 1/8 16 5/8	35 1/8 36 5/8	10	20 5/16	20 7/8	20 5/8	313	313(2P) 316
404T 405T			6 1/8 6 7/8		13/16	7 1/2	2 7/8	7 1/4	3/4					16 5/8	36 7/8						
444U 445U	7 1/2	9	7 1/4 8 1/4	1 1/4	13/16	9 1/8	2 7/8	8 5/8	3/4	3	19 9/16	16	21		40 5/8 42 1/8	11	22 7/8	24 1/4	23 5/16	313	313(2P) 319
444T 445T			7 1/4 8 1/4			8 15/16	3 3/8	8 1/2	7/8					19 1/2	42 3/4						
447T			10											23	46						

NEMA frame sizes standardize dimensions to allow easy replacement of motors by different manufacturers. (Courtesy of Baldor Motors)

Figure 2-3 NEMA Frame Dimensions (inches) (Cont.)

449 FRAME

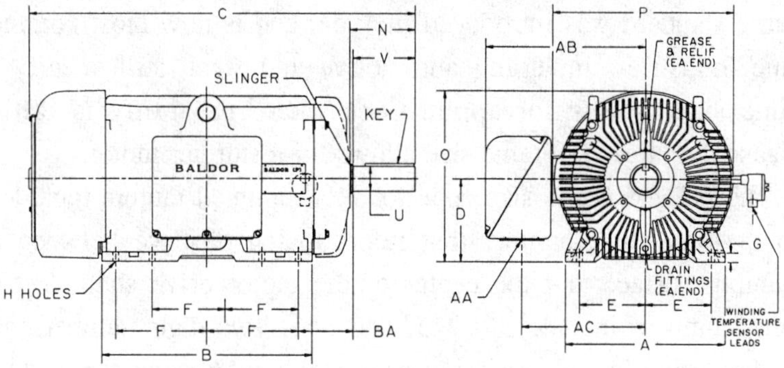

5000 FRAME

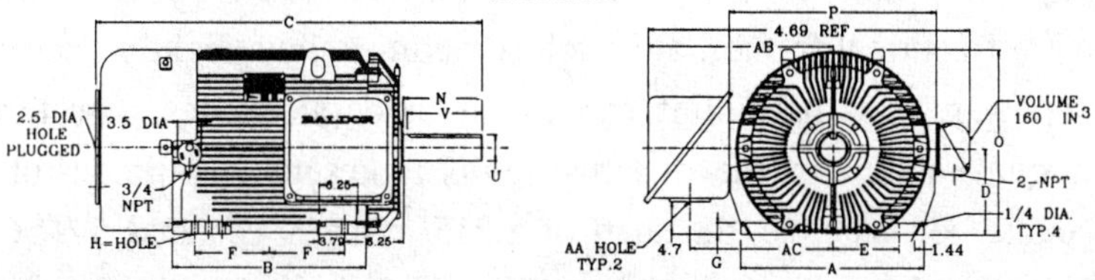

NEMA FRAME	FOOT MOUNTING					SHAFT DIMENSION				CONDUIT BOX			FRAME						BEARINGS	
	BA	E	2F	G	H	N	U	V	KEY	AA	AB	AC	A	B	C	D	O	P	ODE	DE
449T	7½	9	10	1¼	13/16	8½	3⅜	8¼	⅞	4 NPT	21¾	16¾	21¾	28¾	52⅝	11	22⅞	24⅝	314	319
5007L	8½	10	11	1¾	⅞	11⅝	3⅞	11⅛	1	4 NPT	26⅞	20 13/16	25⅝	28⅜	56⅝	12½	26⅞	29⅞	314	314
5009L			14											34⅜	62½				222	322
5011L			18											42⅜	70½				222	324

NOTE: Standard Bearing ODE = Opposite Drive End, DE = Drive End.

standard frame specifications allow motors from different manufacturers to be used interchangeably with the same mounting hardware.

The NEMA **U-Frame** standard was introduced in 1952. The **T-Frame** standard was introduced in 1964, and is now most common. Some industries, including automotive and steel, still specify U-Frame size motors for applications where reliability is critical because the larger U-Frame size allows for a sturdier motor.

The NEMA frame size code for foot mounted motors includes a two or three digit number that refers to the distance between the mounting surface and the center of the motor drive shaft. Typical frame numbers include 56, 215, and 365. Two-digit numbers give this dimension in $1/16$" units. For example, in a 56 frame this distance is $3^1/2$" ($16 \times 3.5 = 56$). By NEMA definition, two-digit frame numbers are fractional frames, although sometimes they slightly exceed 1 horsepower, and three-digit frames are integral frames. For three-digit frame numbers, the first two digits represent this dimension in $1/4$" units. For example, the shaft of a 215 frame is centered $5^1/4$" ($4 \times 5.25 = 21$) above its mounting surface. The third digit in the frame number indicates whether the frame is short, medium or long. Most

Table 2-2   NEMA Frame Suffixes

Suffix Letter	
C	C-face mounting.
D	D-face mounting.
H	Rigid mounting with a large size base.
J	C-face with threaded shaft for pump applications.
JM	Close-coupled pump motor with specific dimensions and bearings.
JP	Close-coupled pump motor with specific dimensions and bearings.
M	Motor with $6^3/4$" flange for oil burner applications.
N	Motor with $7^1/4$" flange for oil burner applications.
T	T-frame (current design standard).
TS	T-frame with short shaft for belt driven loads.
U	U-frame (older design standard).
Y	Non-NEMA standard mount. Can indicate a special base, face or flange.
Z	Non-NEMA standard shaft.

NEMA frame codes allow motor buyers to quickly identify motors with the same physical dimensions.

Figure 2-4   JP Pump Motor

This JP frame motor is designed for specific pump applications. (Courtesy of Lincoln Electric)

Table 2-3   Selected NEMA Motor Frame Sizes

HP	3600		1800		1200		900	
	U-Frame	T-Frame	U-Frame	T-Frame	U-Frame	T-Frame	U-Frame	T-Frame
1	NA	NA	182	143T	184	145T	225	213T
5	213	182T	215	184T	254U	215T	256U	254T
10	254U	213T	256U	215T	284U	256T	286U	284T
20	284U	254T	286U	256T	326U	286T	364U	324T
50	364US	324TS	365U	326T	405U	365T	444U	404T
100	405US	365US	444U	404T	NA	444T	NA	445T
200	NA	444TS	NA	445T	NA	505UZ	NA	505UZ

The first two digits of the frame size code indicate the height of the center of the drive shaft above the mounting surface in quarter inches. The third digit indicates whether the frame is short, medium or long. Thus, a 256T frame has a shaft centered 6-1/4 inches above the mounting surface, and a longer body than the 254T. Other dimensions, such as the location of mounting bolts, are also standardized for each NEMA frame size.

integral frame codes include one or two letter suffixes after the number as described in Table 2-2.

Not all motors are produced to NEMA frame sizes. Small motors, large motors, and custom designs for use in a specific piece of machinery are not built to NEMA frame standards. The following designs are not NEMA designs:

- **C-** and **D-Face** motors bolt directly onto a piece of machinery by their drive face. Although NEMA frame numbers do not apply to these frames, they are often described to by their equivalent NEMA frame number. Some motors can be converted to C- and D-Face by changing their end plates.
- Vertical shaft motors are designed to stand on one end. They are common in pumping applications. Because the pump shaft weight is borne by the motor bearings in some applications, these require special designs
- Motors built to other standards, such as the IEC Metric standards for frame dimensions (Figure 2-5).

SUMMARY

There are many different types of electric motors. Three-phase, squirrel cage induction motors are the most common in industrial and commercial applications. This class includes a large number of specific designs and models. Squirrel cage induction motors offer the greatest potential for cost effective energy savings. Anyone who works with motors should become familiar with NEMA motor design and frame size standards which apply to most three phase motors sold in North America.

Figure 2-5 IEC Motor Frame Dimensions

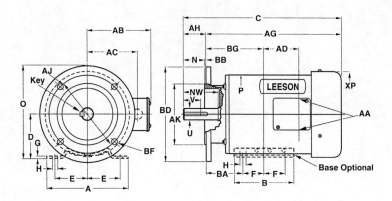

IEC Frame	Mounting					Shaft						B14 Face/B5 Flange					General			
	2E	2F	BA	D	H	U	AH	KEY	SA	R	TAP	AJ	AK	BD	BF	BB	AB	XP	B	O
63	100	80	40	63	7	11	23	19	4	9.0	M4	75° 115°°	60° 95°°	90° 140°°	M5° 9°°	2.5° 3.0°°	116	96	96	108
71	112	90	45	71	7	14	30	26	5	11.5	M5	85° 130°°	70° 110°°	105° 160°°	M6° 9°°	25° 3.5°°	114	130	105	132
80	125	100	50	80	10	19	40	33	6	16.0	M6	100° 165°°	80° 130°°	120° 200°°	M6° 12°°	3.0° 3.5°°	124	149	127	151
90S	140	100	56	90	10	24	50	36	8	20.5	M8	115° 165°°	95° 130°°	140° 200°°	M8° 12°°	3.0° 3.5°°	135	182	152	173
90L	140	125	56	90	10	24	50	36	8	20.5	M8	115° 165°°	95° 130°°	140° 200°°	M8° 12°°	3.0° 3.5°°	135	182	152	173
100L	160	140	63	100	12	28	60	41	8	24.5	M10	130° 215°°	110° 180°°	160° 250°°	M8° 15°°	3.5° 4.0°°	135	182	176	173
112M	190	140	70	112	12	28	60	41	8	24.5	M10	130° 215°°	110° 180°°	160° 250°°	M8° 15°°	3.5° 4.0°°	162	231	176	225

ALL DIMENSIONS IN MILLIMETERS (1 inch = 25.4mm)

Chapter 3

Motor Efficiency

It is not exactly correct to say that motors *consume* electricity. Electric motors *convert* electrical energy to mechanical power. This conversion is never perfect. A portion of the input energy is lost as heat. The ratio of mechanical energy output divided by the electrical energy input is called *efficiency*. Increasing motor efficiency means that a given amount of electrical power input produces more mechanical power output. Equation 3.1 shows three ways to calculate efficiency.

$$\text{Efficiency} = \frac{\text{Output}}{\text{Input}} = \frac{\text{Input - Losses}}{\text{Input}} = \frac{\text{Output}}{\text{Output + Losses}} \quad (3.1)$$

Electrical power is measured in watts, abbreviated *W*. The relatively large amounts of energy used by three-phase motors are measured in kilowatts (1,000 watts), abbreviated *kW*. In some parts of the world, motor mechanical output is also measured in kilowatts, but in North America output is measured in horsepower. One horsepower equals 746 W, or 0.746 kW. For this reason, we use a conversion factor of 0.746 when comparing electrical input power and horsepower output power in efficiency calculations.

Since *increased* efficiency *decreases* the amount of energy need-ed to produce a given power output, efficiency values are inverted, or placed in the denominator, in calculations of motor energy use. The basic equation for motor electrical consumption is:

Demand (kW) = hp x L x 0.746 x 1/Eff.   (3.2)

Where
kW   = Motor energy consumption in kilowatts.
hp   = Motor rating in horsepower.
L   = Load factor.
0.746 = Conversion factor from horsepower to kilowatts.
Eff. = Motor efficiency.

The equation above uses decimal fractions of load and efficien-cy, such as *0.87*. If load and efficiency are in percentage units, such as *87%*, we divide these values by 100. Below is the equation for motor energy consumption as it is usually written:

Demand (kW) = hp x L/100 x 0.746 x 100/Eff.   (3.2)

Where
kW   = Motor energy demand in kilowatts.
hp   = Motor rating in horsepower.
L   = Load factor (percentage of full-load).
0.746 = Conversion factor from horsepower to kilowatts.
Eff. = Motor efficiency rating (percentage).

In later chapters we will use this equation to calculate motor energy consumption, operating costs, and the value of improved motor efficiency. At this point just note that a motor's energy con-sumption is affected by its size (horsepower rating), load (load fac-tor), and efficiency.

Example:

The electrical consumption of a 50-horsepower motor with an efficiency of 91.4% at 3/4-load is:

$$\text{Demand} = 50 \times 75/100 \times .746 \times 100/91.4 = 30.6 \text{ kW}$$

The electrical consumption of an energy efficient model with an efficiency of 94.2% is:

$$\text{Demand} = 50 \times 75/100 \times .746 \times 100/94.2 = 29.7 \text{ kW}$$

MOTOR LOSSES

Energy losses are the determining factor in motor efficiency. These losses can be segregated in five classes, described in Table 3-1. Two of these classes are called fixed losses because they are not greatly affected by the motor load. The other three increase with load and are called variable losses (Figure 3-2).

Figure 3-1   Comparison of Losses From Standard and Energy Efficient Models (5 Horsepower, 1800 RPM)

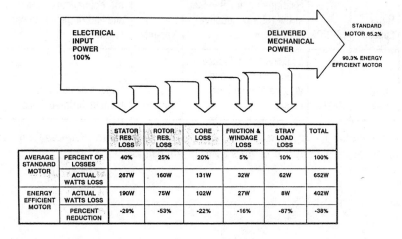

		STATOR RES. LOSS	ROTOR RES. LOSS	CORE LOSS	FRICTION & WINDAGE LOSS	STRAY LOAD LOSS	TOTAL
AVERAGE STANDARD MOTOR	PERCENT OF LOSSES	40%	25%	20%	5%	10%	100%
	ACTUAL WATTS LOSS	267W	160W	131W	32W	62W	652W
ENERGY EFFICIENT MOTOR	ACTUAL WATTS LOSS	190W	75W	102W	27W	8W	402W
	PERCENT REDUCTION	-29%	-53%	-22%	-16%	-87%	-38%

This illustrates the typical energy flow of standard and energy efficient motors at full load. (Courtesy of Baldor Motors)

Table 3-1   Classes of Motor Energy Losses

Name	Percent of Total Losses	Description	Fixed or Variable	How to Reduce
Core Losses	15-25%	Energy required to magnetize core.	Fixed	Improved permeability (silicon) steel, lengthening core, using thinner laminations in the core.
Windage & Friction	5-15%	Losses due to bearing friction and air resistance, which is primarily caused by the cooling fan.	Fixed	Lower friction bearings, improved fan design and air flow. Since efficient motors produce less waste heat a smaller fan can be used, further reducing losses.
Stator Losses	25-40%	Heating due to current flow (I) through the resistance (R) of the stator winding. Often referred to as an I^2R (I-squared-R) loss.	Variable	Increasing the volume of copper wire in the stator, through improved stator slot designs, and by using thinner insulation.
Rotor Losses	15-25%	Heating due to I^2R losses in the rotor conductive bars.	Variable	Increasing the size of rotor conductive bars and end rings to reduce resistance.
Stray Load	10-20%	Leakage fluxes induced by load currents and various other minor losses.	Variable	Various design and manufacturing details.

Total motor energy losses have five main components. Reducing any of these losses increases a motor's overall efficiency.

Figure 3-2   Losses Versus Load

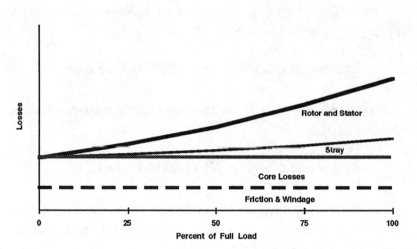

Rotor and stator I²R losses, and stray load losses increase as motor load increases. Core losses, friction and windage are relatively constant, or "fixed."

While each of these losses represent a relatively small portion of the energy used by the motor, their total is significant. These losses waste energy and produce heat. Because heat accelerates the aging of insulation and bearings, these losses reduce motor durability and reliability.

Motor losses can be calculated using this equation:

Losses (kW) = hp x L/100 x 0.746 x (100/Eff. - 1)   (3.4)

Where
kW   = Motor energy losses in kilowatts.
hp   = Motor rating in horsepower.
L   = Load factor (percentage of full-load).
0.746 = Conversion factor from horsepower to kilowatts.
Eff.   = Motor efficiency (percentage).

Example:

Here is the energy loss calculation for a 50 horsepower motor with an efficiency of 91.4 at 3/4-load.

Losses = 50 x 75/100 x .746 x (100/91.4 -1) = 2.6 kW

Here is the energy loss for an energy efficient model with an efficiency of 94.2.

Losses = 50 x 75/100 x .746 x (100/94.2 -1) = 1.7 kW

The losses from a typical 50 horsepower motor equal the energy consumed by 26 100-Watt light bulbs. An energy efficient model can reduce these losses by over 1/3.

RANGE OF MOTOR EFFICIENCIES

Electric motors are available in a range of efficiencies. Motor efficiency varies depending on design, size, load and operating conditions. Figure 3-3 shows the range from minimum to maximum efficiencies for commercially available motors at different horsepowers. The dashed line labeled "Typical" indicates the efficiencies of the standard models that are most commonly purchased.

MOTOR EFFICIENCY TESTING STANDARDS

Although efficiency is a simple concept, measuring and comparing motor efficiency can be challenging. It is important that users understand and use uniform efficiency definitions and standards when comparing motor performance. There are several different motor testing standards which prescribe specific procedures, such as what test equipment may be used, how long the motor is to run prior to testing, how loads are to be applied, what data are to be collected, and how various losses are to be measured. Table 3-2 shows test standards for medium size induction motors that are used in different parts of the world.

Figure 3-3   Motor Efficiency Range

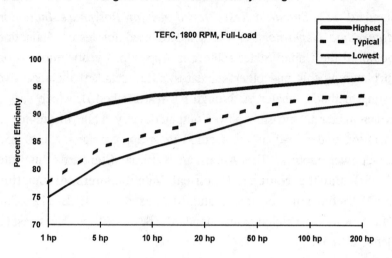

Efficiency for both standard and energy efficient motors tends to increase, and the range narrow, at higher horsepowers. Therefore, what is considered high efficiency for a small motor may be low efficiency for larger motors. The dashed line labeled Typical indicates the efficiencies of the most commonly purchased models.

Table 3-2   Motor Testing Standards

United States	Institute of Electrical and Electronic Engineers	IEEE 112
United States	American National Standards Institute	C50.20 (based on IEEE 112)
United States	National Electrical Manufacturers Association	MG1-12.58.1 (based on IEEE 112)
Canada	Canadian Standards Association	C-390
International	International Electrotechnical Commission	IEC 34-2
Japan	Japanese Electrotechnical Committee	JEC-37
Great Britain	British Standards	BS-269

Be sure to compare motor efficiency based on the same or equivalent test standards. Most motors sold in the U.S. are tested according to NEMA MG1 (based on IEEE 112) and motors sold in Canada are tested according to C-390. These two tests now yield identical results and can be used interchangeably.

The Institute of Electric *al* and Electronic Engineers (IEEE) Standard 112, *Standard Test Procedures for Polyphase Induction Motors and Generators*, is the standard used for testing induction motors in the United States (note: see Appendix I-vi for information on obtaining this and other standards). This standard includes five testing methods, labeled A through F. Test Method B, which uses a dynamometer to measure power output directly while the motor is operating under load, is the method most appropriate for 1 to 250 horsepower motors. The American National Standards Institute (ANSI) and the National Electrical Manufacturers Association (NEMA) have motor test standards based on IEEE 112. The Canadian motor efficiency test standard CSA C-390 produces results identical MG1.

to Figure 3-4   Motor Testing Using Dynamometer

Dynamometer testing is the most common and accurate method of measuring induction motor efficiency. Specialized testing laboratories are able to obtain results within ±0.2 percentage points. (Photo courtesy of Lincoln Electric)

MOTOR TESTING METHODS

A. *Brake.* A mechanical brake is used to load the motor while the torque and speed are measured to calculate load. Since a mechanical brake produces a significant amount of heat, this method is limited to small motors.

B. *Dynamometer.* A dynamometer is an instrument that maintains a constant torque resistance, allowing motor load to be calculated. Dynamometers can measure loads up to a few hundred horsepower, depending on their size. This is the recommended method for testing performance of motors in the 1 to 250 horsepower range.

C. *Duplicate Machines.* This method uses two identical motors coupled together. One is operated as a motor while the other becomes a generator, returning power back to the electrical grid. Efficiency is measured by dividing the total losses by two.

D. *Input Measurement.* The motor is tested when loaded and unloaded without measuring exact output power. Voltage, current, electrical power, speed, temperature, and winding resistance are measured. Core, I^2R, Friction and Windage losses can be calculated from this data. Stray Load losses are either assumed to be a specific percentage of output, or are determined using special tests (reverse-rotation and rotor-removed). This method is used when a suitable dynamometer is not available.

E. *Equivalent Circuit.* Various no-load and locked-rotor tests are performed to provide data for calculating Core and I^2R losses. Friction and Windage are estimated, and Stray Load losses are either estimated or determined as in Method D. This is usually the least accurate way to calculate motor efficiency because such a large portion of losses are not directly measured.

Some motor test standards differ in how they treat stray load losses. CSA C-390 and IEEE 112, Method B determine these losses using special tests. The IEC Standard 34.2 assumes stray load losses to be fixed at 0.5 percent of input, while JEC-37 assumes no stray losses. Since stray load losses represent 8% to 15% of total losses, estimating or ignoring these losses reduces the accuracy of efficiency testing. The same motor can have efficiency ratings that differ by several percentage points depending on which test method is used (Table 3-3).

Table 3-3   Efficiency Ratings For the Same Motors Tested
With Various Standards

Standard	7.5 Horsepower Motor	20 Horsepower Motor
IEEE-112, Method B	80.3	86.9
CSA C-390	80.3	86.9
IEC - 34.2	82.3	89.4
BS - 269	82.3	89.4
JEC - 37	85.0	90.4

U.S. and Canadian motor efficiency testing methods yield the same results, but those from other countries tend to underestimate stray-load losses and are therefore not comparable.

Performance testing of medium and large size motors is difficult and expensive. Motor testing requires an industrial laboratory with specialized equipment operated by skilled staff. Each motor must be connected to the dynometer and power supply, then run until it reaches normal operating temperature. Loads of 25%, 50%, 75%, 100%, 125% and 150% are applied while electrical input energy is measured with a wattmeter. During the test a substantial amount of mechanical energy is converted into heat by the dynamometer, requiring a large cooling system. Because of the many steps and checks involved, testing a single motor can take a full day and cost hundreds or thousands of dollars.

Efficiency tests are performed under carefully controlled conditions, so they usually indicate the motor's highest efficiency. A motor may not perform as efficiently during actual operation. As we will see in later chapters, a variety of factors can reduce efficiency, including improper repairs or maintenance, under- or over-voltage, phase unbalance, and other electrical power quality problems.

MOTOR EFFICIENCY DEFINITIONS

Motor testing standards specify how individual motor tests should be performed. Accurate motor testing is too time consuming to be performed on all motors, so ratings are used based on tests of a statistical sample of the model population. The efficiency of individual motors can vary from their rating as a result of normal variations in materials, manufacturing processes, and test procedures. The efficiency definitions described below define the relationship between a motor's rating and efficiency test results.

1. *Tested.* This refers to the efficiency measured by testing that specific motor. This is the best indication of a motor's performance, but testing is too expensive to perform for each individual motor, so tested efficiency is seldom available.

2. *Nominal* or *Average Expected.* These terms are identical and are the preferred rating to use when comparing motors because they are relatively accurate and widely available. Nominal values are the average value obtained after testing a sample population of the motor model. *Nominal* means "in name only," referring to the small expected performance variation between individual motors of the same model due to random variations in materials and production. Any specific motor is unlikely to perform at exactly its nominal rating since 50% of motors should test slightly higher and 50% should test slightly lower than that point.

3. **Nameplate.** NEMA standard MG1-12.58.1 specifies that efficiency and losses be determined in accordance with IEEE
   Standard 112, Method B. Full-load efficiency results are then
   stepped down to the next lowest value on NEMA MG1 12-8
   (Table 3-4 below). For example, if a motor model's nominal

Table 3-4   Nominal and Minimum Nameplate Efficiency Values (Percent)

Nominal	Minimum	Nominal	Minimum
96.2	95.4	87.5	85.5
95.8	95.0	86.5	84.0
95.4	94.5	85.5	82.5
95.0	94.1	84.0	81.5
94.5	93.6	82.5	80.0
94.1	93.0	81.5	78.5
93.6	92.4	80.0	77.0
93.0	91.7	78.5	75.5
92.4	91.0	77.0	74.0
91.7	90.2	75.5	72.0
91.0	89.5	74.0	70.0
90.2	88.5	72.0	68.0
89.5	87.5	70.0	66.0
88.5	86.5	68.0	64.0

*The left columns are efficiency values allowed for NEMA motor nameplates.
If a model's average efficiency is not on that list, the manufacturer uses the
next lower value. For each nameplate efficiency there is a lower Minimum
Efficiency in the right column, which represents the lower end of the range
of expected variation. Note that the gaps between values increase as you go
lower on the list. (Excerpt from NEMA Table MG1 12-8, previously 12.6A)*

efficiency is measured at 94.1%, that value would be used on its nameplate because 94.1% is in the table. But if the tested efficiency values average 94.0%, the manufacturer must use a nameplate efficiency of 93.6%, the next lowest value. This approach was established in the early 1980's to avoid the implication that efficiency values were accurate to the nearest 0.1%. However, this rounding of values reduces precision and is less justified now due to improvements in motor efficiency testing accuracy.

4. *Minimum.* These values, which are also published in NEMA MG 12-8, are intended to represent the lowest point in the bell curve of motor efficiency distribution, indicating the minimum efficiency that a buyer can expect from a given motor, even if it is among the least efficient of that model's production run. (Figure 3-5)

5. *Calculated.* Sometimes motors cannot be dynamometer tested, so efficiency is calculated based on testing to isolate specific losses and design parameters (test methods E and F). This is an inferior way to determine motor efficiency. If this is the only data available on a motor you should consult an independent motor expert for evaluation of efficiency calculation methods.

6. *Apparent Efficiency.* This is the product of a motor's efficiency and power factor. With this definition, energy consumption can vary considerably depending whether efficiency is high and power factor is low, or vice versa. This can be deceptive since efficiency tends to have a much greater impact on energy costs than does power factor. Apparent Efficiency should never be used to compare or evaluate motors.

Figure 3-5   Motor Efficiency Distribution Curve

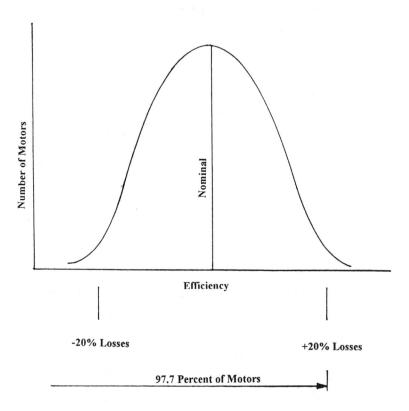

Nominal ratings represent the middle efficiency value. Due to random per-formance variations, half of all motors have slightly lower losses, and half have slightly greater losses. The Minimum Efficiency rating represents the low end of the efficiency curve. Less than 2.3% of motors should perform below this efficiency.

HOW MANUFACTURERS CALCULATE MOTOR PERFORMANCE RATINGS

1. A representative sample of each motor model is tested by the manufacturer using the IEEE 112-B testing standard in the United States, or CSA C-390 in Canada. Test results differ slightly due to random production and testing variation. For example, a manufacturer may measure the following full-load efficiencies for nine individual motors of the same model:

   91.3, 91.5, 91.4, 91.4, 91.6, 91.2, 91.4, 91.3, 91.5

2. The manufacturer averages these to 91.4. Since 91.4 is not in Table MG 12-8, the next lower value is selected, which is 91.0. This *Nominal Efficiency* value is stamped on that model's nameplate. Although the manufacturer is limited to using only values from the NEMA Table on the motor nameplate, they may publish a more accurate value in their catalog and technical literature. Thus, published values may differ from those on the nameplate.

3. The corresponding *Minimum Efficiency* value of 89.5 is selected. This may also be stamped on the nameplate.

4. The IEEE 112-B protocol specifies testing for efficiency, power factor and other operating values at 25%, 50%, 75%, 100%, 125% and 150% loads. These values are also averaged for each model. Manufacturers may supply this data in their catalogs or upon request, but are not required by NEMA to include it on motor nameplates.

5. As production of the model continues the manufacturer performs spot checks. If results begin to vary from the original the manufacturer may "rerate" the motor's nameplate values every few years.

EFFICIENCY AND LOAD FACTOR

Imagine that you are comparing the fuel efficiency of new cars. Would you be interested in fuel consumption at each car's top speed? At 65 miles per hour? At 40 miles per hour? During stop-and-go driving? Of course, you want to compare automobile fuel consumption based on normal driving conditions. The fuel consumption at 120 miles per hour isn't normally used for comparing cars, even if a model can go that fast, because it does not represent typical driving. Similarly, electric motor efficiency should be evaluated under typical operating conditions.

Since motor efficiency varies with load factor, as will be discussed in Chapter 4, motors should be compared using the efficiency rating closest to their average loading. Two motors may have the same full-load efficiencies, but significantly different efficiencies at the load level at which they actually operate. Although full-load efficiency ratings are often used for motor comparisons, this is an inaccurate measurement for most applications. Before you buy a motor, determine the expected operating load factor and use appropriate efficiency rating data for comparing models. Most, but not all manufactures provide full-, 3/4-, 1/2- and 1/4-load data. Even if this information is not in the catalog, it may be available in the MotorMaster Software database of motor performance, or on request from the manufacturer's engineering office.

MOTOR RATING ACCURACY

How accurate are motor tests? How much variation exists between individual motors of the same model and manufacturer? How honest are manufacturers in their efficiency claims? These are important questions that we are only beginning to be able to answer.

Motor testing and rating is performed primarily by manufacturers. In the early 1990's, a few independent motor testing facilities were established in North America, including the Industrial Electrotechnology Laboratory in North Carolina, a motor testing laboratory at Oregon State University in Corvallis, Oregon, and the Laboratorie des Technologies Electrochimiques Et des Electrotechnologies in Quebec. These independent test laboratories are starting to provide useful information about the quality of manufacturers' performance data.

These specialized testing laboratories are able to produce consistent and verifiable results within ±0.2 percentage points when the same motor is tested at different facilities, although less precision can be expected from manufactures' production line testing results. A series of "round robin" tests, in which the same motors were tested by different manufacturers to determine the accuracy of their testing procedures, showed variations of up to 1 percentage point between the highest and lowest measured values for the same motor.

Currently available independent test data indicate that motor manufacturer's nameplate efficiency values are usually close to actual test results. Virtually no new motor tested has failed to meet its Minimum Efficiency rating.

Although some variation can be expected between motor ratings and actual performance, ratings can be used with confidence to compare motors for purchase decisions. As the independent laboratories test more motors and publish the results, motor researchers and buyers will have even more information from which to base decisions.

EFFICIENCY OF OLDER MOTORS

It is often necessary to determine the efficiency of older motors when evaluating potential savings from replacing them with a more efficient model. Unfortunately, there is currently no easy way to measure the efficiency of operating motors, and more research is needed to provide estimates of motor efficiency depending on motor type, age and history. Here are some guidelines to help you estimate the efficiency of older motors.

Studies of motors that had previously been repaired show a reduction in average efficiency ranging from 0 to 2.5 percentage points. The value of this efficiency decrease tends to converge at about 1 point for motors under 100 horsepower, and about 0.5 percentage points for larger motors. Recent tests indicate slightly less reduction in the efficiency of energy efficient motors but further study is needed to confirm these results.

Recent tests of used motors, most of which have been rewound one or more times, suggest that, on average, older motors in the 25 to 150 horsepower range are about 5 percentage points less efficient than new energy efficient motors. The difference in efficiency between old and new energy efficient motors is typically greater than 5 percentage points for motors that are smaller than 25 horsepower. The lower efficiencies of older motors probably result from a combination of motor design improvements in new motors and damage inflicted on the motor during repairs.

Average motor efficiency has increased over the last 50 years, especially since the early 1970's, as shown in figures 3-6 and 3-7. Notice that 1950's U-Frame motors were more efficient than the first generation of T-Frame motors introduced in the mid-1960's. The T-Frame redesign of 1964 was intended to provide a smaller, cheaper-to-build motor. At the time, energy efficiency was a low priority to motor manufacturers and purchasers. Energy price increases in the 1970's prompted motor manufacturers to improve energy efficiency.

Figure 3-6 Motor Efficiency Changes with Frame Redesigns

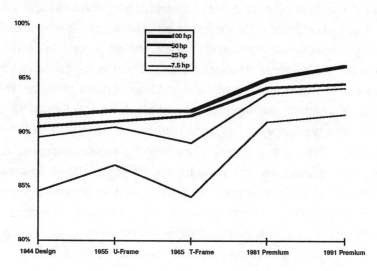

The efficiency of some motor classes decreased when T-Frames were first introduced in the mid-1960's. These motors were designed for low production costs and small size; efficiency was a minor concern at that time. Average motor efficiency has since improved in all motor classes.

Figure 3-7 Typical Full-Load Motor Efficiencies, 1980 to 1990

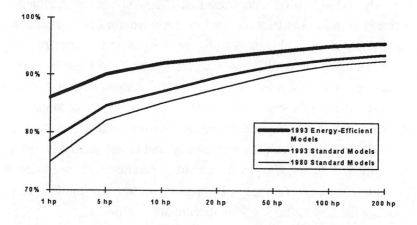

Typical efficiency for standard motors has increased since 1980 due to improved designs and manufacturing standards. Even higher efficiencies are available from energy efficient motors. These curves illustrate general trends and do not apply to any specific motor class.

Now, even standard T-Frame motors are as efficient as U-Frame models, and premium efficient motors are significantly more efficient.

The second reason for the lower efficiencies of older motors is the high incidence of damage during the rewind process, as will be discussed in Chapter 9. The stator core lamination insulation can be damaged if overheated during the winding burnout process. This source of potential damage was not widely known before 1981 so motors that were rewound prior to that time are likely to have lost efficiency. Overheating is still a problem if a repair shop does not take proper precautions or hurries the rewind process. Core loss testing should be performed prior to major repairs to identify low performance motors. A number of other factors, including changes to winding patterns and wire size, changes to bearing type, and changes to the air gap can also cause reductions in motor performance.

SUMMARY

It is important to understand what motor efficiency means and how it is measured. It is essential to use a consistent efficiency standard to guarantee that you compare apples to apples. The IEEE 112-B standard is a specific protocol for performing each motor efficiency test. The NEMA MG1 and Canadian C-390 efficiency standards define how individual tests are used to create Nominal and Minimum efficiency ratings. Other standards are used in other parts of the world, but they are so different that the results should not be compared directly against those based on North American test standards.

Since motor efficiency varies with load, it is important to use an efficiency rating that represents the application's actual load factor. Full-, 3/4-, 1/2- and 1/4-load efficiency values are available from motor manufacturers. Chapter 12 provides specific recommendations for obtaining performance information, comparing models and selecting the best motor for your specific applications.

Chapter 4

Motor Performance Characteristics

This chapter describes various motor performance characteristics including torque, speed and horsepower. An understanding of these factors is critical for choosing the best motor for a particular application and optimizing motor system efficiency.

TORQUE

The rotational force produced by a motor is called torque. It is measured in pound-feet, which is the amount of force that would be experienced on a lever one foot long bearing one pound of weight. Torque can be either static (not moving) or active (moving). An active force produces mechanical power.

Torque requirements vary considerably from one motor application to another, and are often a critical design feature. Many applications, such as centrifugal pumps and fans, have **variable torque**, requiring relatively little torque when they accelerate from a stop and when operating at slow speeds. Other applications have **constant torque** loads. For example, a conveyor requires about the same torque whether it moves at 20 or 200 feet per minute. These place the greatest load on the motor when accelerating from a stop or operating at low speeds. Some applications such as rock crushers have high **peak loads** during operation.

There are four different types of minimum motor torque ratings that relate to different points on a motor's speed-torque curve (Figure 4-1)

Figure 4-1   Typical Motor Speed-Torque Curve

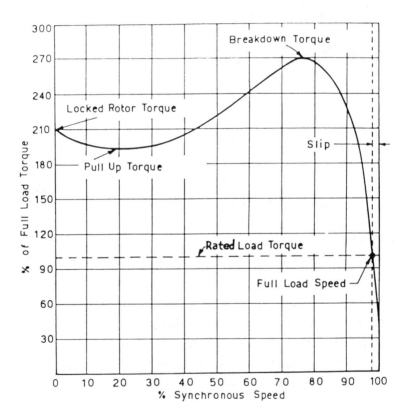

This illustration shows the four common motor torque definitions as they relate to motor speed for typical NEMA design A and B motors. (Courtesy of Lincoln Electric)

1. *Rated* or *Full-Load Torque.* This is the torque at the motor's rated load and speed.
2. *Locked-Rotor Torque.* This is the maximum torque that the motor can produce from a dead start. In many applications, such as conveyors and other process equipment, this is a critical design factor.
3. *Breakdown Torque.* This is the maximum torque that the motor can produce when operating without stalling. This is a critical feature in applications that experience occasional extreme loads, such as saws or crushers.
4. *Pull-up Torque.* This is the minimum torque developed during acceleration between zero and full speed. It is the lowest point on the torque curve. It is seldom a critical design factor.

As was described in Chapter 2, NEMA has established motor design classes with different torque characteristics, listed in Table 4-1.

NEMA designs A and B have moderate locked-rotor torque. These are ideal for centrifugal load pumps and fans, in which full

Table 4-1   Motor Design Torque, Current and Slip Characteristics

Design	Locked-Rotor Torque (Percent F.L.)	Starting Current (Percent F.L.)	Full-Load Slip (Percent F.L. RPM)	Breakdown Torque (Percent FL)
A	medium (70-275%)	no limit (600-900%)	low (1-5%)	high (175-300%)
B	medium (70%-275%)	medium (600-700%)	low (1-5%)	medium (175-300%)
C	high (200-250%)	medium (600-700%)	medium (5%)	medium (190-225%)
D	highest (275%)	medium (600-700%)	highest (5-8%)	high (275%)

NEMA motor design classes have different torque, current and slip characteristics.

torque only occurs when the motor reaches full speed. These represent the majority of induction motor applications.

Design C and D motors produce higher locked-rotor torque. They are suitable for applications with fixed torque and fluctuating loads. Typical fixed torque applications include conveyers, cranes, fixed displacement compressors, process equipment and machine tools. Locked-rotor torque ratings are the major consideration in these applications. It is often possible to use a smaller motor by selecting a design C or D motor rather than a design A or B for high

Figure 4-2   Typical Torque Curves for NEMA Design A, B, C & D Motors

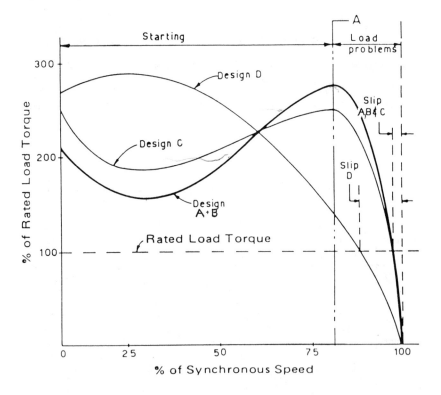

Torque characteristics vary among the NEMA motor Designs. It is important to select the design that is intended for an application's load. (Courtesy of Lincoln Electric)

locked-rotor torque operations. This can reduce purchase costs, increase motor reliability, and in some cases increase operating efficiency. Consult a mechanical engineer or motor vendor for advice on which motor design to select for any application with high torque requirements.

Energy efficient motors exhibit approximately the same torque characteristics as a comparable standard motor, but check individual motor performance characteristics before selecting any motor if this is a critical design factor.

MOTOR SPEED

There are three types of motor speeds to consider:

1. *Synchronous Speed*

Synchronous speed is the rotation speed of the motor's magnetic field. The synchronous speed of an induction motor depends on the electrical supply's frequency (60 Hz in North America, and 50 Hz in other parts of the world) and the number of "poles," as shown in Table 4-2. The formula for synchronous speed is:

Synchronous Speed = 120 x frequency / number of poles   (4-1)

Table 4-2   Induction Motor Synchronous Speed

Number of Poles	60 Hertz	50 Hertz
2	3600	3000
4	1800	1500
6	1200	1000
8	900	750
10	720	600
12	600	500

A motor's magnetic field rotates at synchronous speed. Synchronous speed is a multiple of the line frequency, which is normally 60 Hertz in North America. Under load, an induction motor actually operates slightly slower than its synchronous speed.

Most induction motors have 2, 4 or 6 poles, with 4 pole (1800 RPM) being the most common. Slower motors of the same horsepower have larger frames. This is because slower motors produce much higher torque to achieve the same power output, so larger frames are needed to handle the increased force.

2. *Operating Speed*

Induction motors only operate at their synchronous speed when they are unloaded. The rotor lags slightly behind the magnetic field as the load on the motor increases. **Operating speed** is a motor's actual speed under any specific condition. **Slip** is the difference between synchronous speed and actual speed. Because motor speed decreases with load, slip increases with increased load.

3. *Full-Load Speed*

Most motors have a Full-load RPM rating stamped on their nameplate. This is the speed at which the motor is expected to turn when operated at its rated load, and is typically 1% to 4% slower than synchronous speed. For example, 1800 synchronous RPM motors often have a F.L. RPM rating of 1760.

A motor's F.L. RPM rating can provide useful information about its performance and operating conditions. But, like other manufacturers' ratings, this value is based on tests performed on a representative sample of each motor model. Some manufacturers publish actual measured operating speeds, but the numbers stamped on the NEMA Nameplate are usually rounded to the nearest 5 RPM. For these reasons, the F.L. RPM rating of a particular motor often deviates from its actual performance.

Operating speed is a critical factor in the efficiency of centrifugal load equipment, such as pumps and fans, which are designed and "tuned" to operate at a specific RPM. Even a small change in operating speed can significantly affect their performance and efficiency. This is especially important if a centrifugal pump or fan is operating

Figure 4-3 Motor Speeds

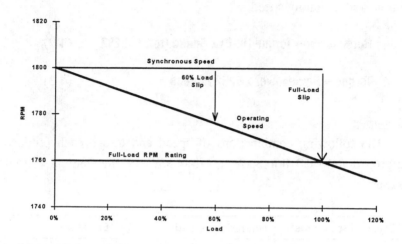

Operating Speed decreases as load increases. The difference between Synchronous Speed and Operating Speed is called "slip."

at less than full load due to an oversized motor, in which case the operating speed is even higher than specified. In Chapter 12 we will explore how to select replacement motors for centrifugal load applications to insure that their operating speed maintains optimum efficiency.

LOAD AND HORSEPOWER

Load is defined as the mechanical output of a motor. Load is measured in **horsepower** in North America and in **kilowatts** in most other parts of the world. A motor's horsepower rating indicates the maximum mechanical power output it should normally produce. NEMA has established 24 standard ratings from 1/2 to 400 horsepower. [ignores ratings > 500 hp]

Horsepower is a function of torque and rotation speed. At any given speed, torque is proportional to horsepower. As a motor's speed increases, less torque is required to produce a given load. The following equations describe the relationships between horsepower, torque and operating speed:

Horsepower = Torque (lb-ft) x Speed (rpm) / 5252   (4-2)

Torque = Horsepower x 5252 / Speed   (4-3)

Example:

The following combinations of speed and torque each produce approximately 10 horsepower (7.46 kW) of mechanical output power:

Torque (pound-feet)	Operating Speed	Equation
14.8	3540	(14.8 x 3540)/5252 = 9.97
29.8	1760	(29.8 x 1760)/5252 = 9.99
45.3	1160	(45.3 x 1160)/5252 = 10.0
60	880	(60 x 880) / 5252 = 10.05

In practice, motors seldom produce exactly their rated horsepower. The proportion of actual output to rated output is called **load factor.** For example, a water pump may require 8 horsepower (6.0 kW) of energy to achieve a desired rate of flow. If a 10 horsepower motor was used, it would have a load factor 80%. A 15 horsepower motor driving the pump would have a 53% load factor. A 20 horsepower motor would have a 40% load factor. A 7.5 horsepower motor would have a 107% load factor.

Most modern motors can operate with a load factor greater than 100%, at least for short periods. This ability to operate overloaded without failing is indicated by a multiplier called **service factor.** A 1.15 service factor rating indicates that a motor can operate at 15% over its rated load without immediately failing. For example, a 10 horsepower motor with a 1.15 service factor could drive a load up to 11.5 horsepower.

SERVICE FACTOR

The service factor of a motor indicates how much over that model's rated horsepower it can operate without immediately failing. Most new motors have 1.15 service factors, due to high quality insulation materials that can withstand higher temperatures. However, before you overload all of your motors to take advantage of these high service factors here are some things that you should know:

- Most motors are inefficient when operated above their rated horsepower. Most motors have peak efficiency at 3/4-load. Higher load factors reduce efficiency.

- Although motors will not fail immediately when operating between their full-load rating and their service factor rating, they will probably have a shorter operating life.

- Power quality problems, such as low voltage, harmonics or voltage unbalance, will eliminate the margin provided by a high service factor.

Think of operating a motor above rated load like having employees work overtime. It's a handy option for accommodating unusual circumstances, but expensive, inefficient and leads to staff burnout.

For these reasons it is best to avoid sizing motors to operate at more than their rated horsepower except for short time periods, even if allowed by their service factor. Use a high service factor as an indication of a high quality, more reliable motor.

RELATIONSHIP BETWEEN LOAD AND PERFORMANCE

Figure 4-4 shows the typical relationships between motor load and four performance characteristics.

Figure 4-4   Typical Motor Performance as a Function of Load

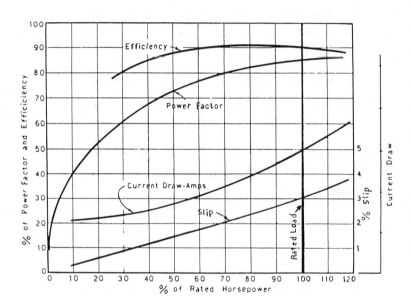

Motor load affects operating characteristics, including efficiency, power factor, current draw and slip.

Figure 4-5 shows the typical relationships between motor load and efficiency for four motor sizes. New motors 5 horsepower or larger tend to be most efficient with 60% to 80% load factors. Small motors' efficiency tends to peak close to full-load, and decreases quickly at lower loads.

Of course, not every motor behaves like this. Some motors in the same size, speed and enclosure class may peak at full-load, while others peak at 3/4- or 1/2-load, as shown in Figure 4-6. Therefore, it

Figure 4-5   Typical Motor Efficiency as a Function of Full Load

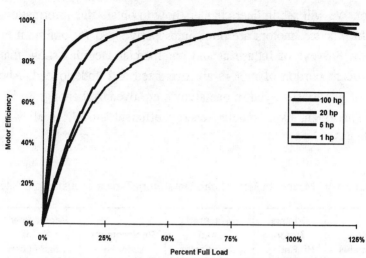

Motor efficiency varies with load. Large motors are usually most efficient in the 60% to 100% load range, while small (under 5 horsepower) peak closer to full-load.

Figure 4-6   Part-Load Motor Efficiencies

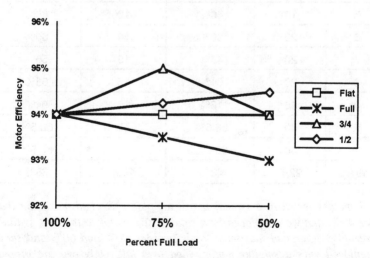

*Motors with the same full-load efficiency may perform differently at part-load. The curve labeled **Flat** has the same efficiency at each load level. The curve labeled **Full** peaks at full-load, 3/4 peaks at 75% load, and 1/2 peaks at 50% load. Compare motors based on the load factor closest to which they will actually operate, not just on full-load efficiency values.*

is important to use individual performance data when selecting a motor. We will see in later chapters how to obtain this information.

In practice, motors are often improperly sized for optimum efficiency. Surveys of industrial and commercial facilities show that a significant portion of motors are oversized and underloaded. About half of motors surveyed in one study were oversized enough to justify replacement by a smaller, energy efficient model, as shown in Table 4-3.

Table 4-3   Maximum Motor Load Data From Typical Industrial Facility

Motor Number	Original Motor HP Rating	Measured Load (Load Factor)	Replacement Motor HP	Replacement Motor Load Factor
1	10	53%	7½	71%
2	15	36%	7½	72%
3	15	32%	7½	64%
4	15	34%	7½	68%
5	15	46%	10	69%
6	20	30%	10	60%
7	20	42%	15	56%
8	20	51%	15	68%
9	40	16%	10	64%
10	40	66.5%	40	66.5%
11	40	66.5%	40	66.5%
Average	**22.7**	**43%**	**15.3**	**66%**

Of 11 motors tested in a typical industrial plant, five had maximum loads under 40%, and were replaced by a smaller size motor at the next available opportunity. Four had maximum loads between 40% and 60% and should be replaced with a smaller motor when they fail. Only two are properly sized for efficiency. (Example provided by Robert K. Hoshide)

There are several reasons for oversizing motors, some of which are legitimate, and some which indicate poor engineering:

- *Variable loads*

  Motors should be sized to accommodate the greatest expected load. If a motor is sized for a peak that seldom or never occurs, it may operate inefficiently most of the time. Pumps and fans that usually operate with load factors less than 80% are good candidates for an adjustable speed drive or other speed control strategy to improve efficiency. These are discussed in Chapter 8

- *Motor is "derated" due to poor operating conditions.*

  If a motor is used under extreme duty conditions, such as at high altitude or poor power quality, oversizing the motor allows it to operate cooler and thus more reliably. However, there may be other, more efficient strategies to maintain reliability, such as improving power quality or providing better cooling.

- *Motor was resized during repair.*

  Sometimes maintenance staff will replace a failed motor with a larger size if the correct size was not available, or if they believe that will increase reliability. This reflects poor planning. Motors should only be resized if justified by careful engineering analysis.

- *Careless design.*

  Motors are often oversized because of upgrading at several stages during the design process. Here's a typical scenario:

  1. A design engineer determines that a pump will impose a maximum 10 horsepower load. To be safe, he indicates a 15 horsepower motor in the design specifications.
  2. The supervising engineer changes that to a 20 horsepower motor, "to be safe."
  3. Not knowing that the motor is already oversized, the review engineer upgrades to a 25 horsepower motor, "to provide an extra margin of comfort."

4. The purchasing agent chooses a 30 horsepower motor, because "it's such a good value."

The result of all of these "upgrades" is a more expensive, less efficient motor. Motors with load factors of 40% or less and relatively steady loads are often cost effectively replaced by a smaller, more efficient model. Methods to help you evaluate these options are explained in later chapters.

LOAD ACCELERATION

Some motor applications have operating cycles that include numerous starts and stops, or widely fluctuating loads that require frequent acceleration. This consumes power at much higher rates than when the motor operates at its constant rated load, in addition to placing mechanical and thermal stress on the motor. Since motor acceleration usually lasts for just a few seconds it adds little to the overall energy consumption of motors in typical applications which cycle only occasionally. But some applications, such as elevators and lifts, require motors to constantly accelerate and decelerate. There are two ways to optimize efficiency and reliability in these situations:

1. Choose a high-slip motor. Design D motors have high slip, which allows them to accommodate widely varying loads efficiently and with minimal stress. Although these motors are inherently less efficient at any specific load level, their ability to accelerate a load efficiently means that they may be more efficient overall in applications that involve constant load changes.

2. Minimize dynamic (moving) mass. The greater the mass the motor must accelerate, the more energy it will require, and the higher torque rating the motor will need.

Applications that have frequent on-off cycles or wide load fluctuations should be carefully evaluated to identify the best motor, taking into account maximum torque requirements and motor acceleration efficiency. In some cases, alternative equipment designs that minimize dynamic mass should be considered to reduce motor loads.

DETERMINING MOTOR LOAD FACTOR

It is important to determine the load factor of your motors in order to insure that the motor is properly sized for its application, and to help identify potential problems. There are two methods of determining load factor. The **Electrical Method** compares the electrical input energy measured by a wattmeter with the motor's rated load. This is most accurate. Another technique, called the **Slip Method**, compares the operating speed measured by a tachometer with the motor's Full-Load RPM rating. This approach is not recommended due to inaccuracies in F.L. RPM ratings that can significantly affect results, unless its accuracy is first confirmed, as described below.

1. Electrical Method Load Testing

Using a power meter (wattmeter) you can determine the electric power going into the motor and compare this with the motor's nameplate output power. An accurate power meter is necessary for load testing, rather than a simple ammeter because current is not a valid measurement of motor load below about 60% of full-load, due to the large portion of reactive power. The wattmeter must be true RMS, which prevents inaccuracies due to variations in power quality. Appropriate power meters cost a few hundred to several thousand dollars, depending on features. When properly calibrated they are typically accurate to ±2%. A recording power meter (data logger) is especially useful for variable load applications.

The formula for calculating motor load is:

$$\text{Load Factor (Percent)} = \frac{\text{Input power [kW] x Efficiency (\%)}}{\text{Rated Horsepower x 0.746}} \quad (4\text{-}4)$$

Efficiency values can be obtained from the motor nameplate, manufacturer's data, or MotorMaster software. Use typical efficiency values for comparable motors if more specific data is unavailable. If a motor is very old or has been rewound, you should subtract another

1-3 points from the efficiency estimate. Any inaccuracy in your estimate of motor efficiency will create a proportional inaccuracy in
your load factor measurements. For example, if you consider your
efficiency estimate accurate within ±5%, and your meter is accurate
within ±2%, then your load factor estimate can be considered accurate within ±7%.

*Note: Electrical testing is potentially hazardous. It should
be performed only by trained personnel using proper precautions.*

2. Slip Method

As explained earlier in this chapter, slip is the difference
between a motor's synchronous speed and operating speed, as shown
in equation 4-5.

Slip = Synchronous Speed - Operating Speed   (4-5)

Example:

A 4 pole (1800 RPM synchronous speed) motor has a Full-Load
RPM rating of 1750.

F.L. Slip = 1800 - 1750 = 50

Slip is approximately proportional to load. For example, the slip
of a motor operating at 3/4-load is about 75% of its full-load slip,
and at 1/2-load the slip is 50% of its full-load slip. This is comparable to determining how full a truck is by measuring its speed going
up a hill: the more weight (load) the truck carries, the slower it goes.
If you measured a truck's speed going up a hill when unloaded and
fully loaded, you could roughly estimate if it is partially loaded,
assuming that all other factors are held constant. The formula to calculate operating load from slip is:

Load Factor (%) = (Operating Slip/Full-Load Slip) x 100 (4-6)

Example:

A 4 pole (1800 RPM synchronous speed) motor has a Full-Load RPM rating of 1750 and a measured operating speed of 1775 RPM.

Load Factor = [(1800 RPM - 1775) / (1800 - 1750 RPM)] x 100
= 25/50 x 100
= 50%

The slip method is the easiest way to measure load, but is often inaccurate because:

- Motor nameplate Full-Load RPM ratings (a critical value in the formula) are often inaccurate due to variations in motor testing and manufacturing, and are rounded to the nearest 5-RPM.

- A rewind or other repair can change a motor's performance.

- Power quality problems (off-voltage, phase unbalance, etc.) and temperature affect motor operating speed.

- A combination of inaccuracies can occur in either the manufacturer's or tester's instrumentation or testing procedures.

For these reasons, the slip method should only be used on a particular motor after its accuracy (actually, the accuracy of the motor's F.L. RPM rating) is confirmed by testing the same motor with a power meter (wattmeter) as described earlier. If the two methods provide similar results you can use the slip method to track motor load factor in the future. If the two methods do not agree, that motor's actual F.L. RPM can be calculated by measuring the motor speed at full load as determined by the wattmeter. This value can then be used for future slip method calculations.

SUMMARY

Motor torque, speed, and load are interrelated and affect motor efficiency and reliability. It is important that you understand the various, often confusing terms used to measure these performance factors. The following guidelines can help you optimize your motor system.

- Size motors to operate in the 50% to 100% load range as much as possible.

- Carefully determine anticipated loads when designing equipment in order to select the proper size motor.

- Use adjustable speed drives or other engineering strategies with variable load to avoid operating oversized motors.

- Only use the overloading ability of high service factors for occasional short periods since loading motors beyond their rating reduces operating efficiency and life.

- Test motor load factor using a wattmeter. This information will help you identify motors that are improperly sized for early replacement or resizing when the motor fails. If wattmeter and slip method tests provide similar results you can rely on the slip method for measuring that motor's load factor in the future.

- Use multiple tests or a recording wattmeter on motors that have varying loads to chart the full load cycle.

Chapter 5

Electric Power Supply

Think of electricity as food for your motor. And just as you wouldn't feed a work horse unhealthy food, it is important that motors receive good clean electric power. This chapter identifies how you can "tune" your electric power to optimize motor system performance. It covers voltage, frequency, phase balance, harmonics, power factor and resistance losses.

The National Electrical Code and technical organizations such as NEMA have established standards for electric motor power quality (note: information on these standards and how to obtain them is provided in Appendix I). In order to maximize motor efficiency and reliability, however, you may want to use tighter electrical performance standards than are usually prescribed. Most electrical performance standards are intended primarily to guarantee safety and short-term reliability. The tighter standards recommended here are intended to also maximize motor system efficiency and long-term reliability.

VOLTAGE

Voltage is analogous to the pressure in a water system. Increased voltage means that a given amount of current (amps) produces more power (watts). There are three voltage definitions that relate to electric motors:

1. *Supply* or *Nominal Voltage.* This is the voltage at the transformer. Most facility distribution systems supply 120, 208, 240, 480 or 600 Volts, although this may be adjusted slightly by changing the transformer taps.

2. *Rated* or *Design Voltage.* This is the voltage at which a motor is designed to operate. Because voltage decreases with distance from the transformer, electrical equipment is normally designed to operate with a voltage slightly lower than the Supply Voltage: 110, 200, 230, 460 or 575 Volts. Many motors are designed to operate at either of two voltages, depending on how their leads are connected. The most common motor rating is 230/460, which means that the motor can operate either at 230 or 460 Volts. Generally, a motor will provide approximately the same performance at either voltage, although input current will be double at the lower voltage rating.

3. *Operating Voltage.* This is the actual input voltage at the motor. It should be the same, or very close to the motor's Voltage Rating.

Voltage that is either too high or too low tends to reduce motor system efficiency and have other negative impacts on motor performance (Figure 5-1), although the exact effect depends somewhat on the specific motor design.

In practice, few motors operate at exactly their rated voltage, and NEMA standards state that motors should be designed to accommodate ±10% voltage, or a total combined voltage and frequency variation of 10%. Although motors are designed to operate in this range without failing immediately, operating at the extreme ends of this range reduces motor efficiency and long-term reliability. This is especially important if the motor is subject to other types of stress, such as overloading, voltage unbalance or high ambient temperatures. A 3%

Figure 5-1   Effect of Voltage Variation on Motor Performance

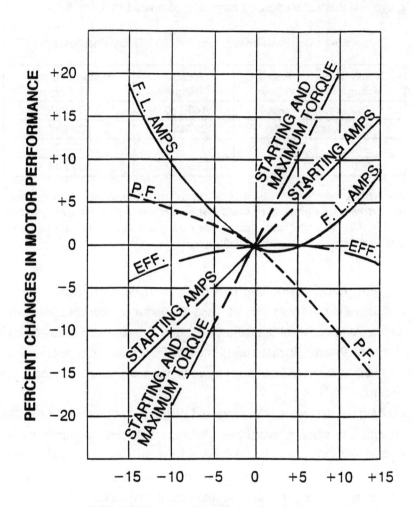

PERCENT VOLTAGE VARIATION

Motor efficiency, power factor and current are all affected by voltage level. Note that efficiency decreases with either under- or over-voltage.

maximum variation from the voltage rating is a better goal. NEMA's range and this recommended range are compared in Table 5-1.

Table 5-1   Common Voltages for 1 to 500 Three-Phase Motors

Nominal Voltage	Rated Voltage	NEMA Range	Recommended Range
208	200	180-220	194-206
240	230	207-253	223-237
480	460	414-506	446-474
600	575	517.5-632.5	535-592

The NEMA range represents a 10% voltage variation. A motor operating at the extreme of this range should not immediately fail, but will perform poorly. The Recommended Range based on a 3% maximum voltage variation improves efficiency and reliability.

Most transformers have taps that can be changed to adjust their output voltage. These can be used to optimize the voltage at the motor. Automatic voltage adjustment may be needed if loads on the electrical system fluctuate significantly. Power factor correction can also help reduce voltage drops by reducing reactive current loads on circuits.

Voltage decreases with increased distance from a transformer. To prevent low voltage, avoid long distances between the supply transformer and the motor. If distribution lines on a circuit are too long, voltage may be too high for motors close to the transformer and too low at the far end. In that case, the circuit may need to be reconfigured, or another transformer may be needed to maintain optimal voltage at all motors. Be sure to follow good design practices and safety rules when modifying and adjusting power systems.

Many manufacturers produce "tri-voltage" motors rated at 208/230-460. This means that the motor can be wired for either 230 or 460 Volts, and when wired for 230 can handle a 208 Volt system within NEMA's allowable ±10% voltage variation. Although tri-voltage motors may operate at 208 Volt, they will not operate as efficiently or reliably as a motor designed for that voltage. Since voltage drops with increased distance from the transformer, a motor operating on a 208 Volt system will usually experience an actual voltage somewhat lower, typically closer to 200 Volts, which is beyond acceptable voltage variation. Tri-voltage motors operated on 208 Volt systems will usually have a lower efficiency, run hotter, slip more, produce less torque and have a shorter operating life than a motor designed for this voltage. For this reason, use a 200 Volt rated motor on a 208 Volt system, rather than a tri-voltage design.

FREQUENCY

Frequency indicates how many cycles (Hertz) per second the electrical flow alternates. The standard frequency in North America is 60 Hz, while other parts of the world use 50 Hz. Induction motors can operate within ±5% of rated frequency, although a significant frequency variation is likely to reduce efficiency and reliability. Over-frequency increases speed and power factor, while locked-rotor torque and current decrease. Under-frequency increases torque and

Table 5-2   Effects of Frequency Variation on Motor Performance

Characteristic	105%	95%
Locked-Rotor Torque	-10%	+11%
Maximum Torque	-10%	+11%
F.L. Slip	+10 to 15%	-5 to 10%
F.L. Efficiency	Small Increase	Small Decrease
F.L. Power Factor	Small Increase	Small Decrease
Full-Load Current	Small Decrease	Small Increase
Starting Current	-5%	+5%
Operating Temperature	Small Decrease	Small Increase

A small variation in line frequency can affect motor performance in many ways.

current, while speed and power factor decrease. In most electrical systems frequency seldom varies enough to cause a problem.

PHASE BALANCE

A racing shell moves with beautiful grace when all oars are pulled with equal power and in perfect time. If one oar is out of synch or cannot match the others' effort the boat moves inefficiently. It is equally important for the three phases of an electrical system to be of equal voltage and current. Voltage unbalance reduces motor efficiency and creates distribution system losses. It also leads to current unbalance, which cause torque pulsations, vibrations, mechanical stress on the motor and overheating of the windings. This can significantly reduce motor efficiency and durability.

Phase voltage balance should be within 1 percent when calculated using this formula:

$$\text{Percent Voltage Unbalance} = \frac{\text{Maximum Difference from Average Voltage x 100}}{\text{Average Voltage}} \qquad (5\text{-}1)$$

For example, if voltages on the three phases of a motor are 462, 463 and 455, the average is 460. The voltage unbalance is (460-455 / 460) x 100 = 1.1%. Unbalance of 1% or more requires derating the motor according to NEMA standard MG1-14.35 (Figure 5-2) and will void most manufacturers' warranties. A 10 horsepower motor with a 2.5% voltage unbalance would be derated by .925, and therefore should be loaded with a maximum 9.25 horsepower load. A voltage unbalance of only 3.5% can increase motor losses by 20-percent. Unbalances of 5% or more indicate a serious problem in the electrical distribution system.

There are several common causes of voltage unbalance:
- Unevenly distributed single phase loads on one or two phases.
- Unequal resistance in distribution system wiring.
- Unequal motor winding reactance.

Figure 5-2   Voltage Unbalance Derating, based on NEMA MG1-14.35

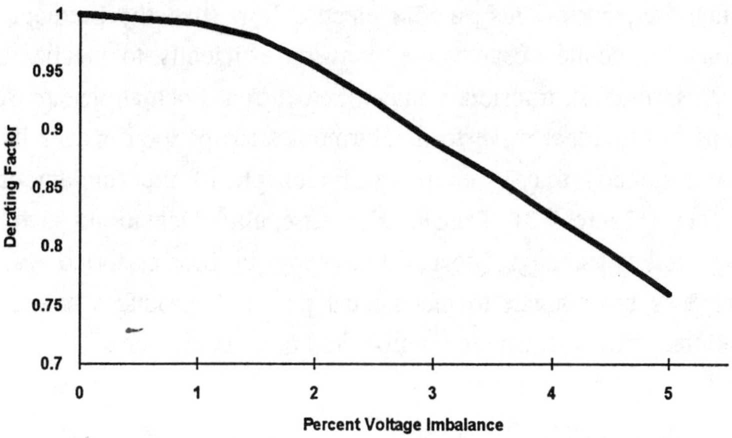

Unbalanced voltage reduces a motor's efficiency, producing excess heat. The motor must be derated as indicated to avoid overheating.

- Poor connections or ground faults on one phase.
- Unbalanced or unstable utility supply.
- Faulty operation of power factor correction equipment.
- An open circuit on the distribution system primary.

To minimize voltage unbalance you should:

1. Monitor voltages on all phases at each motor to check for voltage unbalance.
2. Check electrical system line drawings to verify that single-phase loads are uniformly distributed or limited to dedicated circuits.
3. Install required ground fault indicators.
4. Perform thermographic and circuit testing described in Chapter 10 to identify potential problems.

HARMONICS AND TRANSIENTS

Motors are designed to operate with a sinusoidal wave form of constant frequency. This smooth electric flow, like the predictable motion of a gentle ocean wave, converts efficiently to mechanical power. Harmonics, transient voltage, and current fluctuations are distortions of this ideal wave form. Harmonics are periodic waves having a frequency that is an integral multiple of the fundamental frequency (Figure 5-3). Transients are irregular fluctuations such as voltage spikes and sags. Most of the energy in these distorted waveforms does not convert to mechanical power. It produces heat and vibrations which can damage motors and other equipment.

Figure 5-3   Harmonic Distortion of AC Electric Current

Harmonics

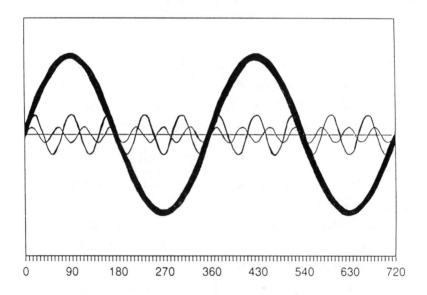

This graph shows a 60 Hz Fundamental wave with 5th and 7th harmonics. Harmonic distortion can cause various problems, including reduced energy efficiency, increased operating temperatures, and tripping of electrical protection devices.

There are many causes and types of power wave distortions, including lightning strikes, switching within the electrical system, short circuits, and inverters which are used to power many types of electronic equipment. Since motors have a high inrush current during startup, they are a common cause of voltage sags and other short term fluctuations. Adjustable Speed Drives (ASDs) often produce 5th, 7th, 11th and 13th harmonics, although this problem is reduced by design improvements in most newer models.

The Institute of Electrical and Electronics Engineers (IEEE) publication 519, 1992, *Recommended Practices and Requirements for Harmonic Control in Electric Power Systems* establishes standards for electric power distortion. Section 10 of this document, "Recommended Practices for Individual Consumers" describes current distortion limits within industrial facilities. A variety of strategies and hardware can be used to reduce harmonics and transients to acceptable levels, including reconfiguring loads on a circuit, harmonic trap filters, and isolation transformers.

Here are the general steps to prevent and solve harmonic problems:

1. As much as possible, place motors and other large induction loads on a circuit separate from electronic equipment such as computers, electronic ballasts and ASDs.

2. Select electronic equipment with low harmonic distortion ratings. Computers, electronic ballasts and ASDs are now available with design features that minimize harmonic impacts, as defined in IEEE 519-1992 Table 10.3.

3. Soft start controllers can be used to limit motor inrush currents, preventing voltage sags.

4. Identify sources of harmonics within your system. This may be done by simply switching various pieces of equipment on and off to identify when problems occur, or you may need to use a transient detector recorder.

Due to their complexity, projects to address harmonic problems should be overseen by an electrical engineer who has experience in power conditioning.

POWER FACTOR

Induction motors require both **real power** (also called **active power**) and **reactive power**. The real power, measured in kW, is converted to work or heat. The reactive power, measured in kVAR (kilovolt amperes reactive), produces the motor's magnetic field, and is stored and discharged in the electrical circuit. **Apparent power** (also called **total power**) is the product of total voltage and total current, and is measured in kVA (kilovolt amperes). The ratio between real power and total power is called **power factor**. Power factor can be indicated either as a decimal fraction such as .90, or as a percent such as 90%.

Power factor indicates the relationship between voltage and current cycles. If voltage and current cycles are in synch, the power factor is 100% and the system produces no reactive power. If current cycles follow voltage, the power factor is said to "lag." If current is ahead of voltage, power factor is said to "lead." In either case, the power factor is reduced below 100%. Purely resistive loads such as heaters, stoves and incandescent lighting have a power factor of 100%. Motors, transformers, and some types of lighting (neon, mercury vapor, fluorescent, etc.) cause a low power factor. Capacitors, and some types of equipment such as synchronous motors have high or leading power factor. Lagging power factor can be corrected by incorporating capacitance into the circuit.

Reactive power does not directly consume energy or do work, but by increasing the flow of current, reactive power creates energy losses in the electrical system. This forces electrical utilities to increase the capacity of their distribution system and install power factor compensation equipment. An increasing number of utilities impose a surcharge on customers who have low power factors, typically below 95% or 90% at the main meter. Some utilities bill demand based on kVA, which incorporates reactive power, so electrical costs increase with a power factor below 1.0. These power factor surcharges can be significant, totaling thousands of dollars a year in many facilities. Low power factor can also cost you money in increased distribution losses and by requiring you to upgrade the capacity of your electrical system.

Underloaded induction motors are a major cause of low power factor in most facilities. The amount of reactive power created varies with the size and type of motor, and how much it is loaded. Induction motors often have full-load power factor ratings stamped on their nameplate, and many manufacturers also supply part-load power factor data on request. Full-load power factors are typically

5-4   Power Factor as a Function of Full-Load Amperage

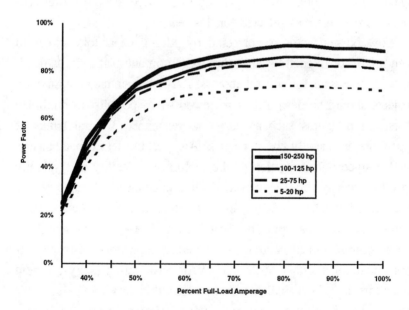

Power factor goes down at part-loads, as measured by percent of full-load amperage. Note low power factors at less than 50% load, especially among smaller size motors. Considerable variation exists among individual models in each motor class, so compare motors based on their specific part-load power factor ratings when available.

between 85% and 95% for large motors, and drop to 50% to 70% for smaller motors at part load. This reduction in part-load power factor is offset by the motor's reduced current, so the total kVA does not necessarily increase in a partially loaded motor. Energy efficient motors tend to have a higher power factor than standard motors, although there is considerable variation between specific models.

Although power factor can reduce efficiency and cost you money, it is not nearly as significant as motor efficiency in terms of energy costs. Energy and capacity charges are typically twenty times greater than power factor charges, and many facilities don't pay for kVAR at all. Power factor can be corrected relatively cheaply. Power factor can be improved in some facilities simply by turning off idling motors, minimizing motors with low load factors, and avoiding operating equipment above its rated voltage. Some equipment, including synchronous motors, can be operated to produce leading power factor and are sometimes selected for this reason.

Low power factor is corrected by adding capacitors, either to each motor, or in central banks that switch on automatically as needed to compensate for several motors. Large power factor correction projects should be designed or reviewed by a specialist to minimize costs and problems such as harmonic resonance. Central banks of capacitors are usually cheaper per kVAR, because less capacitance is needed since only a portion of the motors in a facility are typically operating at any time. However, if all capacitance is located at one location, high currents will still flow through the circuits between motors and the capacitors. In a large facility it may be worthwhile to use a combination of central and dispersed capacitors. Most capacitors consume about 1 Watt per kVAR installed. Energy-efficient capacitors are now available that reduce this loss by about 50%. Capacitors will slightly increase voltage. Harmonic resonance may develop between capacitors and electronic equipment such as ASDs.

Contact an electrical engineer for advice before installing capacitors on a system with ASD, or if you encounter problems such as overheating equipment or tripping switchgear in circuits on which capacitors are installed.

MEASURING POWER FACTOR

There are several ways to measure power factor. A typical multimeter measures apparent power (amps x volts). A more sophisticated meter can also measure reactive power (kVARs). A wattmeter measures real power directly. Since apparent power is the hypotenuse of a right triangle, it is possible to calculate any of these values if you know the other two using the Pythagorean theorem.

Power factor is calculated using these formulas:

$$\frac{\text{Instantaneous}}{\text{Power Factor}} = \frac{\text{Real Power (kW)}}{\text{Apparent Power (kVA)}} \qquad (5\text{-}2)$$

$$\text{Average Power Factor} = \frac{\text{kWh}}{\sqrt{(\text{kWh})^2 + (\text{kVARh})^2}} \qquad (5\text{-}3)$$

Recommendations to reduce power factor costs:

1. Determine whether your facility has low power factor. If so, identify major sources and take corrective action.

2. Avoid idling or oversized, underloaded motors.

3. Consider using synchronous motors for large horsepower, low speed applications if your facility needs power factor correction.

4. If other factors are equal, select motors with the highest power factor rating.

MINIMIZING DISTRIBUTION SYSTEM LOSSES

Since three-phase motors draw a considerable amount of power, even a small amount of resistance in a connection or a leak to ground in a motor circuit can cause serious efficiency and safety problems. Surveys of typical facilities indicate that such problems are not uncommon. There are several steps you can take to minimize resistance, leaks to ground and similar problems. Be sure that the capacity of your electrical system is not exceeded and that all protection devices are working correctly. Power cables that are heavily used should be oversized in new construction or rewiring to reduce resistance losses and voltage reduction. Chapter 10 describes specific methods for identifying common problems in your electrical distribution system.

Transformers are an important part of your electrical system. Like motors, they are available in various sizes and efficiencies. Older, under- or over-loaded transformers tend to be inefficient. These problems can be solved either by installing properly sized transformers or changing circuits to improve loading on existing equipment. In order to optimize your motor system you should:

1. Select transformers that have taps to allow future adjustments.
2. Avoid underloaded transformers.
3. Select energy efficient transformers

SUMMARY

Power quality refers to various features of your electrical power, including voltage, frequency, phase balance, harmonics, power factor and resistance losses. To keep motor systems running efficiently and reliably it is important to monitor power quality in your electrical circuits and make adjustments and modifications needed to correct power quality problems.

Chapter 6

Motor Operating Characteristics

This chapter provides an overview of motor operating characteristics that affect motor reliability and performance, including duty cycle, starting, temperature and operating environment.

DUTY CYCLE

Duty cycle refers to how often and how long a motor operates. This is an important consideration in the selection and operation of motors for several reasons. The more hours a motor operates the more energy it uses, so the more important energy efficiency becomes. A motor with a continuous duty cycle (8,760 hours per year) should be as efficient as possible because of the large amount of electricity it uses. The efficiency of a motor that only operates a few hundred hours a year is less important. To put it another way, motors that operate a large number of hours each year offer greater total energy savings for a given efficiency improvement than motors with shorter duty cycles.

Some applications require motors to idle (operate with no load) for significant periods of time. Turning off idling motors is one way to save energy by eliminating no-load losses and low power factor. Idling motors typically consume 5% or more of their full-load power (watts), and have power factors in the 10% to 20% range, causing them to draw relatively high current (amps). However, stopping and restarting stresses a motor, especially motors used in applications with high locked-rotor torque requirements.

An application's duty cycle is a factor in determining which motor design is appropriate. Most integral three-phase induction motors are designed for continuous operation. They fail prematurely if subjected to the thermal and mechanical stress of too many starts over a short period of time. On the other hand, some motors are intended for intermittent use and will overheat if run constantly because they build up heat during operation. The design duty is stamped on motor nameplates.

Duty cycle can also affect a motor's maintenance and protection requirements. Motors that operate long hours need frequent lubrication. Equipment that sits unused for long periods of time, such as motors that are used seasonally or for backup purposes, should be protected against moisture and other deteriorating influences. Motors can be specified or modified to have internal heaters to prevent condensation, and a variety of special seals for duty cycles that include long periods between use.

STARTUP STRESSES

Starting a motor creates mechanical and thermal stress which can damage the motor, the electrical system and driven equipment. These stresses vary depending on the motor's load and how it is controlled.

Motors experience high **locked-rotor current** (also called **inrush current**) during the first few seconds of startup, which can be several times the motor's operating current. This is why starting a motor often causes a voltage sag which dims nearby lights and can affect other electrical equipment. In some cases, motor inrush current can even trigger electrical overload protection devices. The duration of inrush current is longer for fixed torque applications that take longer to accelerate.

Inrush current also causes heat to build up in the motor and its electrical supply cables. Since the motor's cooling air flow has not yet been established, each motor startup places thermal strain on the motor, especially large motors. Starting also imposes significant mechanical stresses on the motor, motor mounts, and the equipment it drives. Magnetic forces within the motor can induce the windings to vibrate in the stator slots and end turns, which can abrade the insulation system in the coils. For these reasons it is unwise to subject large motors to frequent starts, especially if they drive fixed torque loads.

Applications with high fixed torque loads such as conveyors, machine tools and piston compressors require a motor with a high locked-rotor torque rating. These situations impose the greatest starting stresses. Variable torque loads such as centrifugal pumps and fans impose relatively low locked-rotor torque demands on a motor because high torque does not develop until the equipment approaches its operating speed. Although centrifugal loads impose less startup stress than fixed torque loads, operators should follow appropriate startup procedures and limits in all applications.

To avoid straining the electrical system it is best to stagger the startup of large motors to avoid having more than one start during any one-minute time period. A variety of controls can be used to reduce inrush currents and motor startup stress. These include transformers and other voltage limiting devices, Wye-Start-Delta-Run switches, electronic "soft start" controls which reduce startup current while providing relatively high locked-rotor torques, and adjustable speed drive units. These control systems will be discussed more in Chapter 8.

Be sure to keep duty cycles and starts within the range intended for each motor. In general, motors 200 horsepower and smaller should be subjected to no more than 20 seconds of maximum acceleration time with each start, and should not experience more than a total of 150 seconds of starting power each day. Low inertia loads that accelerate to full speed in a fraction of a second also stress motors, and can result in premature motor failure even when total start-seconds remain low. NEMA has established starting limitation

guidelines for common motor types which are described in publication MG10, *Energy Management Guide for Selection and Use of
Polyphase Motors.* Table 6-1 shows an example of these guidelines.
Check with the manufacturer for the starting limitations of specific
motors and for advice on using motors that have unusual duty
cycles, such as frequent reversing.

Table 6-1   Typical Starting Limitations for Selected NEMA Design B

HP	Maximum Number of Starts	Minimum Off Time (Seconds)
5	16.3	42
10	12.5	46
25	8.8	58
50	6.8	72
100	5.2	110

*Starting a motor imposes electrical, thermal and mechanical stresses which
cause wear and aging. Check with manufacturers or vendors to determine
starting limitations for your specific motors. Be sure that operating staff
understand and observe these limits.*

Will this inrush current effect your electrical demand charge?
Not much. Although electrical consumption during startup is
extremely high, it lasts only a few seconds. Since demand charges
are typically based on a 15-minute measurement, the five- to fifteen-
second inrush current has little impact averaged over this longer time
period.

TEMPERATURE

Excess heat damages motors. High temperatures reduce
motor reliability, durability and efficiency. A 10° C increase in operating temperature will typically reduce a motor's life by half and
bearing life by 25%. About half of motor failures result from degradation of the winding insulation caused by high temperatures. Since

motors produce considerable amounts of heat (the 2.6 kW of waste heat produced by a 50 horsepower motor is comparable to a large electric heater) proper heat dissipation is essential. High operating temperatures also increase watt losses, reducing motor efficiency. For example, a 20° C increase in operating temperature can reduce a typical 50-horsepower motor's efficiency by 0.2%.

To increase motor durability, choose the best quality insulation system. An insulation system consists of insulation on the windings, leads and between phases. There are four motor insulation classes: A, B, F and H. Higher letters indicate significantly increased insulation thermal durability, as shown in Table 6-2. Insulation Classes B and F are most common in mass produced motors. Whenever possible, choose Class F or better insulation. Non-sinusoidal power is especially hard on motor insulation, so specify the best insulation systems on motors used for ASD applications.

Table 6-2   Allowable Maximum Temperature
for Motor Insulation Classes

Class	Allowable Temp Rise Over 40°C Ambient
A	105°C (221°F)
B	130°C (266°F)
F	155°C (311°F)
H	180°C (356°F)

The higher letter insulation classes can withstand more heat without deteriorating and therefore provide greater reliability and durability under given operating conditions.

Motors are designed with an allowable increase in temperature above ambient during operation. This is called **temperature rise**. The total temperature (ambient plus rise) is the **allowable temperature limit**. The maximum temperature rise allowable for a specific motor depends on its insulation class and service factor. Maximum ambient temperature and temperature rise for motors with different service factors and insulation classes are listed in Table 6-3.

Table 6-3   Temperature Limitations for Insulation Classes B and F

Service Factor	Temperature Reference	Class B	Class F
1.0 or 1.15	Ambient Temperature	40°C (104°F)	40°C (104°F)
1.0	Allowable Temperature Rise	80°C (176°F)	105°C (221°F)
1.0	Allowable Temperature Limit	120°C (248°F)	145°C (293°F)
1.15	Allowable Temperature Rise	90°C (194°F)	115°C (239°F)
1.15	Allowable Temperature Limit	130°C (266°F)	155°C (311°F)

This table shows maximum absolute temperature and temperature rise for the two most common insulation classes. The best motors have Class F or H insulation operating with Class B temperature limitations.

For example, a motor with a 1.15 service factor and Class B insulation will not exceed its allowable temperature rise of 194°F (90°C) if ambient temperature is below the 104°F (40°C) limit and altitude above sea level is less than 3,300 feet (1,000 meters). A motor is more reliable if it operates below its rated temperature. For example, a motor operating under Class B service conditions with a Class F or H insulation system is running "cool" relative to its thermal capability. This increases a motor's reliability, and should be specified when purchasing a motor. Energy efficient motors tend to run cooler than standard motors and usually have Class F insulation and a 1.15 service factor, so they can endure higher temperatures and offer longer service life than many standard motors.

Most motors are designed for a maximum ambient temperature of 104°F (40°C) and a maximum elevation above sea level of 3,300 feet (1,000 meters). If these conditions are exceeded, the motor's service factor must be reduced or a larger motor should be used. Since an oversized motor will be underloaded, it runs cooler and avoids damage to windings and bearings. However, significantly oversizing a motor can reduce efficiency, so other cooling options should be explored. Discuss unusual service conditions that a motor might experience with your motor vendor to determine the best model.

CONDITIONS THAT CAN CONTRIBUTE TO MOTOR OVERHEATING.
- Overloading.
- Frequent starting.
- Power Quality problems (improper voltage, harmonics, unbalanced power).
- High ambient temperature.
- High altitude.
- Inverter (ASD) applications.
- Mechanical problems (seized bearings, alignment problems, etc.)
- Poor ventilation.
- Dirt accumulation.
- Accumulated paint.
- Exposure to direct sunlight.

Motors can be specified with overtemperature protection features that turn off the motor if internal temperatures exceed a specified limit. Once the motor cools (and the cause of the overheating is eliminated) the motor can be restarted. There are several types of overtemperature devices. The best design is a thermostat installed at the winding end turns or embedded into the stator slot to sense winding temperature. Since motor windings are the main source of heat, and winding insulation is sensitive to overheating, this is the most critical location for temperature sensing. Thermal sensors can also be installed at bearings. Thermal protection should be specified when ordering motors.

OPERATING ENVIRONMENT

Motors are often exposed to environmental stresses, such as:

- Moisture
- Dirt
- Dust
- Salt
- Corrosive chemicals
- Explosive materials

Figure 6-1   Open Frame Motor

An ODP frame allows air to circulate through the motor for cooling. (Courtesy of Lincoln Electric)

Different enclosures are designed to protect windings from various environmental conditions, including moisture, dust and chemical damage, and to keep objects out of danger from the motor's moving parts. The most common are:

- **Open Drip Proof (ODP)** enclosures allow air to circulate between the inside and outside of the motor for cooling. Drip proof motors have venting designed to prevent drops of liquid from falling into the motor within a 15° angle from vertical. They should be use only in a relatively clean, dry and well-ventilated environment. If installed outdoors, ODP motors should be protected with a cover that does not restrict air flow.

- **Totally Enclosed** motors do not allow air to circulate between the inside and outside of the motor frame, but they are not completely air tight. They are suitable for use in dirty and damp environments. To dissipate heat most enclosed motors have cooling fins and an outside fan at one end. These are called **Totally Enclosed Fan Cooled (TEFC)**. Some smaller enclosed motors do not need a fan, especially if located in the airstream of a fan they drive. These are called **Totally Enclosed Non-Ventilated (TENV)**.

- **Severe Duty** motors are enclosed motors with surfaces treated with non-corrodable materials for use in harsh chemical environments.

- **Wash-down** motors, are enclosed motors designed to be cleaned with water and cleaning chemicals. These are often used in the food processing industries where regular cleaning is essential.

- **Explosion-proof** are enclosed motors designed to prevent sparks inside the motor from igniting flammable or explosive materials outside the motor frame, for use in hazardous environments. The National Electrical Code (NEC) has established categories of motors for various severity of explosion risk. These motors carry an Underwriter's Laboratories (UL) label and may only be repaired by an UL certified shop.

Figure 6-2   Enclosed Frame Motor

*A TEFC frame is enclosed to protect motor components from dirt and mois-
ture. Cooling fins and fan dissipate heat.* (Courtesy of Lincoln Electric)

WHEN TO SEEK ADVICE

It is a good idea to check with the motor dealer, manufacturer, or an experienced engineer for advice if a motor will be operated under any unusual service conditions. These include:

- Poor ventilation, excessive temperature, or high altitude.
- Exposure to dangerous, explosive, combustible, abrasive or corrosive materials.
- Exposure to steam, salt-laden air, or oil vapor.
- Nuclear radiation.
- Abnormal shock, vibration, other external mechanical stresses.
- Abnormal axial, side thrust or torsional impact loads on motor shaft, including operation in an inclined position.
- Excessive deviation from design voltage, frequency, or phase balance.
- Low noise level is required.
- Excessive cycling.
- Reversing or electric braking.
- Locked rotor operation.

SUMMARY

Operating conditions such as duty cycle, startup, temperature and operating environment are important considerations in motor efficiency and reliability. Be sure to match motors to their operating conditions and use the guidelines in this chapter to minimize stress on motors. Choose motors that are designed for an application's duty cycle and avoid excessive startup. Use proper starting procedures. Keep motors cool. If possible use Class F or H insulation and limit the motor temperature rise to that for Class B (130°C). Choose an enclosed motor if it will be operating under damp or dirty conditions.

Chapter 7

Energy Efficient Motors

Most motor manufacturers now produce a special line of **energy efficient** motors. These are sometimes labeled "high efficiency," "premium efficiency," or "energy saving" models by manufacturers. The term **energy efficient** is preferred because it is the term recognized by NEMA as defined in NEMA Standards Publication MG 1-1993 *Motors and Generators*, and because it most clearly describes the feature of interest: energy efficiency.

Energy efficient motors typically reduce losses by 20% to 40%, and cost 15 to 30 percent more than a comparable standard motor. This extra cost is called the **price premium**. Since motors typically consume 5 to 10 times their purchase price each year worth of electricity, or more than 100 times their purchase price during a typical operating life, the price premium of an energy efficient motor is usually repaid many times over. The $1,000 that you spend to buy a 20 horsepower motor is small in comparison to the $100,000 worth of energy it will use during its operating life. A price premium of $150 to $300 is negligible compared to saving 3-percent or more in energy costs, worth thousands of dollars.

Table 7-1   Typical Efficiency and Price Premiums
for Energy Efficient Motors

Horse power	Standard Efficiency	E-E Efficiency	Efficiency Gain	Standard Price	E-E Price	Price Premium
1	77.6 %	85.0 %	7.4 %	$217	$286	$69 (32%)
5	84.0 %	89.2 %	5.4 %	$344	$478	$134 (39%)
10	86.6 %	91.1 %	4.5 %	$614	$780	$166 (27%)
20	88.7 %	92.7 %	4.0 %	$1,024	$1,268	$244 (24%)
50	91.4 %	94.2 %	2.8 %	$2,487	$2,881	$394 (16%)
100	92.3 %	95.2 %	2.9 %	$5,756	$6,775	$1,019 (18%)
200	94.0 %	95.8 %	1.8 %	$10,927	$12,961	$2,034 (19%)

This table shows average efficiencies and typical list prices for standard and energy efficient (E-E), 1800 RPM, TEFC motors in selected sizes. Motor buyers typically pay 25%-50% less than the listed prices. While the size of the efficiency gain for an energy efficient model gets smaller as motor size increases, so does the price premium as a percent of the standard motor price. As a result, energy efficient motors are a worthwhile investment in all motor sizes. As motor size increases so does total energy consumption, so the value of even small efficiency improvements can be significant for larger motors.

Energy efficient motors are available in most NEMA T-Frame motor classes from 1 to 200 horsepower, including speeds of 3600, 1800, 1200 and 900 RPM; ODP, TEFC and explosion proof enclosures; and ratings of 200, 230, 460 and 575 Volts. Custom designed motors can also be specified with energy efficiency features. Purchasers often specify a minimum acceptable efficiency when ordering larger size motors (over 200 horsepower).

Energy efficient motors are premium quality motors. Efficiency gains are obtained through better designs, materials and construction. In addition to saving energy they are usually more durable and reliable. Many motor manufacturers offer a longer warranty for their premium efficient motor lines.

Despite their benefits, only about 15 percent of current electric motor sales nationwide are energy efficient models, and these are primarily bulk purchases by large companies. Many motor buyers are missing potential energy saving and reliability benefits by failing to select energy efficient motors when they are a cost effective choice. Energy efficient motors should be considered in the following situations:

- New installations.
- When ordering equipment packages such as compressors, HVAC systems, and pumps.
- When replacing or upgrading equipment.
- Instead of rewinding a failed motor.
- As part of an energy conservation program to replace lower efficiency equipment.

An energy efficient motor can usually replace a standard model with no modifications. Energy efficient motors tend to have low slip (slightly higher operating speeds and F.L. RPM ratings), and may have relatively high startup current. However, this is not true of all energy efficient motors and it is important to evaluate specific performance features of any motor you buy.

Energy efficient motors are usually the best choice in applications that operate long hours with relatively steady loads, such as pumps, fans and process equipment. Despite their benefits, energy efficient motors are not always cost effective, or may be inappropriate due to specific motor design requirements. We will explore these issues later.

THE ENERGY POLICY ACT AND NEMA ENERGY EFFICIENT MOTOR STANDARDS

The U.S. Energy Policy Act (EPA) of 1992 establishes national energy efficiency testing procedures and standards for electric motors, as well as a variety of other electrical equipment. The EPA gives the U.S. Department of Energy (DOE) authority to prescribe testing and labeling standards for motors, and to fund programs to advance electric motor system technologies.

The Act mandates that most general purpose, 1 to 200 horsepower induction motors built or imported to the U.S. after October 24, 1997 meet the nominal full-load efficiency values shown in Table 7-2. These are the same efficiency values published in NEMA MG1 Table 12-10, and previous to 1993 called Table 12-6C, that a motor must meet in order to be labeled *energy efficient*.[1] The EPA Standard covers NEMA T-Frame, single speed, foot-mounted, continuous rated, polyphase squirrel cage induction motors of NEMA design A and B, either open or closed frame, that are designed to operate on 230/460 Volts and constant Hertz line power, either manufactured alone or incorporated as a component of another piece of equipment. Other motor classes are not currently covered by the Act. Below are examples of motors that are excluded from the minimum efficiency standards:

- NEMA design C and D motors.
- U-Frame motors.
- Motors above 200 horsepower or less than 1 horsepower.
- Vertical mounted motors.
- Motors with more than 6 poles (900 RPM or slower).
- Motors recognized by the USDOE as "special purpose" or "definite purpose" designs.

The Act provides the DOE with the authority to prescribe efficiency standards for small and fractional size motors if it determines that doing so is technologically feasible and economically justifiable. Test procedures for such motors must be prescribed by April 24, 1995, and efficiency standards no later than 18 months later.

The EPA and NEMA standards are higher than the efficiencies of most motors now sold in the U.S., but motors with even higher efficiencies, offering even greater energy savings are currently avail-

---

[1] Prior to 1993, MG 1 Table 12-6B was the NEMA Standard for energy efficient motors, and Table 12-6C was a Suggested Standard for Future Design. In the 1993 edition of MG 1, Tables 12-6B and 12-6C were renumbered 12-9 and 12-10 respectively. NEMA has now designated Table 12-10 as the NEMA Standard and deleted Table 12-9. That change is reflected in Revision 1 of MG 1-1993.

Table 7-2 National Energy Policy Act Efficiency Values

	Full-load Nominal Efficiencies					
	Open Motors			**Closed Motors**		
HP	6 - Pole 1200 RPM	4 - Pole 1800 RPM	2 - Pole 3600 RPM	6 - Pole 1200 RPM	4 - Pole 1800 RPM	2 - Pole 3600 RPM
1	80.0	82.5	-	80.0	82.5	75.5
1.5	84.0	84.0	82.5	85.5	84.0	82.5
2	85.5	84.0	84.0	86.5	84.0	84.0
3	86.5	86.5	84.0	87.5	87.5	85.5
5	87.5	87.5	85.5	87.5	87.5	87.5
7.5	88.5	88.5	87.5	89.5	89.5	88.5
10	90.2	89.5	88.5	89.5	89.5	89.5
15	90.2	91.0	89.5	90.2	91.0	90.2
20	91.0	91.0	90.2	90.2	91.0	90.2
25	91.7	91.7	91.0	91.7	92.4	91.0
30	92.4	92.4	91.0	91.7	92.4	91.0
40	93.0	93.0	91.7	93.0	93.0	91.7
50	93.0	93.0	92.4	93.0	93.0	92.4
60	93.6	93.6	93.0	93.6	93.6	93.0
75	93.6	94.1	93.0	93.6	94.1	93.0
100	94.1	94.1	93.0	94.1	94.5	93.6
125	94.1	94.5	93.6	94.1	94.5	94.5
150	94.5	95.0	93.6	95.0	95.0	94.5
200	94.5	95.0	94.5	95.0	95.0	95.0

This table shows the nominal full-load motor efficiency values prescribed in the 1992 National Energy Policy Act. General purpose induction motors built in the U.S. or imported after October 24, 1997 must meet this standard. These are the same values as NEMA 12-10 standard which defines energy efficient motors. Efficiency testing is performed according to IEEE standard 112, Method B.

able, and their number should increase as manufacturers place more emphasis on efficiency in the next few years. Figures 7-1 and 7-2 show how these standards compare with the efficiency of commercially available motors.

Figure 7-1   EPA/NEMA 12-10 Compared With Efficiency Range

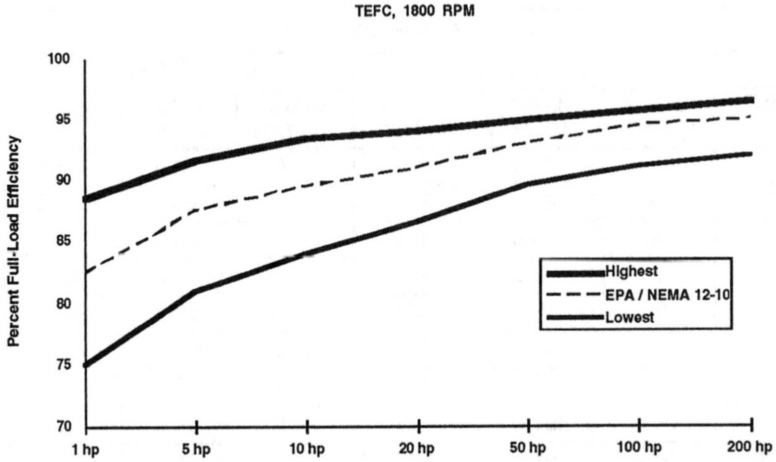

TEFC, 1800 RPM

*This graph shows the range of full-load efficiency ratings for currently avail-
able motors. Also shown is the 1992 Energy Policy Act (EPA) standard,
which has the same values as NEMA 12-10 (previously called 12.6C). The
EPA requires that after October 24, 1997 the most popular types of 3-phase
motors meet this standard to be manufactured in or imported to the U.S.
Motors currently must meet this standard to be labeled "energy efficient."*

   The Energy Policy Act will result in much greater selection and
reduced prices of energy efficient motors. If you are purchasing a
new motor before October 24, 1997 it is important to select a model
which meets the NEMA standard 12-10 for energy efficient motors.
Even better, follow the guidelines in Chapter 12 to identify the most
efficient motor that is cost effective for your application, which may
have an efficiency rating much higher than this standard. Don't rely
on models names such as *premium efficient* or *energy saver.* It is
especially important not to use motors labeled *energy efficient* based
on Table 12-6B, which was the NEMA standard until 1993. Instead,
compare motors based on their actual efficiency ratings. Even after
October 24, 1994 distributors may sell older motors they have in
stock that do not meet the EPA efficiency standard, so continue to

Figure 7-2 Commercially Available Motor Models Currently Meeting
Energy Policy Act and NEMA 12-10 Efficiency Standards

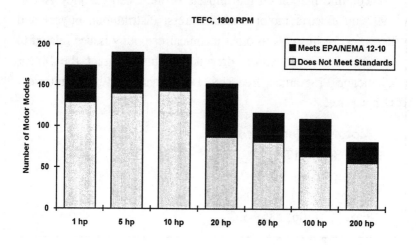

*This graph shows the number of commercially available motor models that
currently meet the Energy Policy Act and NEMA standard 12-10 efficiency
values. Since most motor purchasers tend to buy lower priced models, only
a small portion of motors sold in the U.S. currently meet these standards.
By the end of 1997, most three-phase motors manufactured in the U.S. will
be required to meet this standard as prescribed in the Act.*

check and compare motor efficiency ratings after that date to avoid
being stuck with an "energy hog."

Utilities use a variety of minimum efficiency standards that a
motor must meet to qualify for an efficient motor rebate. Many use
standards higher than NEMA 12-10. Some utilities use a sliding
scale rebate that increases for more efficient motors, rather than a
single standard. Contact your utility to obtain information on rebate
efficiency requirements.

MOTOR EFFICIENCY INFORMATION

For information on the impacts of the Energy Policy Act of 1992 on electric motor manufacturers, distributors, buyers and users, or for answers to other technical or policy issues related to industrial electric motor driven systems, contact the Motor Challenge Program, a free U.S. Department of Energy information service.

Motor Challenge Program
P.O. Box 43171
Olympia, WA 98504-3171
Phone: (800) 862-2086
Fax: (206) 586-8303

DESIGN E MOTORS

The design E motor classification established by NEMA in 1994 has minimum speed-torque and maximum locked-rotor current limits in order to achieve increased efficiency (these torque and locked rotor current values are equivalent to IEC Standard 34-1.) Design E is the only NEMA motor design to have its own efficiency standard. NEMA Standard 12-10 and NEMA design E motor minimum efficiencies are compared in Figure 7-3 and Table 7-3. Because of the high inrush current allowed for design E motors, special electrical protection (fuses and circuit breakers) may be required. However, design E motors may be an appropriate choice for many applications such as pumps and fans which operate long hours and are seldom switched on and off.

ENERGY EFFICIENT MOTOR DESIGN FEATURES

Energy efficient motors tend to be well designed and built, offering increased reliability and durability in addition to energy savings. They don't look any different than a standard motor, but energy efficient motors have several design and production features to reduce losses:

Table 7-3. NEMA 12-10 and Design E Nominal Full Load Efficiencies

1800 RPM				
	Open		Closed	
HP	12.10	Design E	12.10	Design E
1	82.5	86.5	82.5	86.5
1.5	84.0	87.5	84.0	87.5
2	84.0	87.5	84.0	87.5
3	86.5	89.5	87.5	88.5
5	87.5	90.2	87.5	89.5
7.5	88.5	91.0	89.5	90.2
10	89.5	91.7	89.5	90.2
15	91.0	92.4	91.0	92.4
20	91.0	93.0	91.0	93.0
25	91.7	93.6	92.4	93.6
30	92.4	94.1	92.4	94.1
40	93.0	94.5	93.0	94.5
50	93.0	95.4	93.0	95.0
60	93.6	95.4	93.6	95.0
75	94.1	95.4	94.1	95.4
100	94.1	95.4	94.5	95.4
125	94.5	95.4	94.5	95.8
150	95.0	95.8	95.0	95.8
200	95.0	95.8	95.0	96.2
250	95.4	96.2	95.0	96.2
300	95.4	96.2	95.4	96.2
350	95.4	96.5	95.4	96.5
400	95.4	96.5	95.4	96.5
450	95.8	96.8	95.4	96.8
500	95.8	96.8	95.8	96.8

The new NEMA design E motors have nominal full-load efficiencies significantly higher than the current NEMA 12-10 standard for energy efficient motors.

Figure 7-3   NEMA Design E Motor Efficiency Values

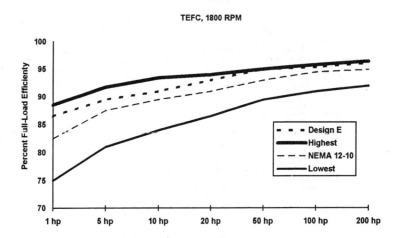

This graph compares the NEMA design E efficiency standard with NEMA 12-10, and existing design A and B motor efficiency ratings. Motors are already commercially available that meet design E minimum efficiencies in most horsepower sizes.

- Higher quality and thinner steel laminations in the stator.
- More copper in the windings.
- Optimum air gap between the stator and rotor.
- Longer rotor.
- Smaller, more efficient cooling fan.

Energy efficient motors have the same frame size as other NEMA models and conform to all other NEMA design requirements, including torque and amperage standards. Energy efficient motors produce less waste heat so they usually run cooler than standard motors. Cooler operating, Class F or better insulation, and high quality bearings used in energy efficient motors increase reliability and operating life. Typical benefits of energy efficient motors include:

- Quieter operation.
- Longer warranties.
- 1.15 service factors.

- Lower idling current and no-load losses.
- Reduced maintenance requirements.
- Better tolerance of thermal stress caused by high ambient temperatures, stalling, frequent starting, or impaired ventilation.
- Increased resistance to abnormal electrical conditions, such as under- or over-voltage, phase imbalance, or imperfect wave shapes.

Not every energy efficient motor has all of these benefits, so check specific motor data when you select motors.

ENERGY EFFICIENT MOTOR
OPERATING CHARACTERISTICS

Energy efficient motors are equal or superior to standard motors in most performance characteristics, such as locked-rotor torque and tolerance of poor power quality. Typical performance differences between standard and energy efficient motors are discussed below. Note that these are general trends and do not always apply. Evaluate each model based on its specific performance data.

1. **Increased Inrush Current**

    Some energy efficient motors are NEMA design A, which means that they can have a higher inrush current than the more common design B. This can cause nuisance tripping of circuit breakers (especially on newer "instantaneous-trip" magnetic circuit breakers) and create overload problems if the motor is on a circuit with limited capacity. This problem can be solved with soft start or ASD controls, discussed in Chapter 8, or by upgrading your electrical system. Consult an electrical engineer knowledgeable of power system applications for advice on dealing with high inrush current problems if they occur.

2. **Torque**

   Energy efficient motors have torque characteristics similar to comparable standard efficient models.

3. **Harmonics and Phase Imbalance**

   Energy efficient motors have Class F or better insulation systems and other design features that are more durable when operated with power quality problems such as harmonics and phase imbalance. However, these problems still reduce motor efficiency and should be minimized in all motor applications.

4. **Operating Speed / Slip**

   Energy efficient motors tend to have less slip than equivalent lower efficiency motors, as shown in Figures 7-4 and 7-5. This small increase in operating speed can affect the efficiency of centrifugal pumps and fans, which are optimized for a specific RPM. Flow is proportional to operating speed, while centrifugal loads increase by the third power (see page 112). This means that a 2% increase in motor speed only increases flow by 2%, but requires 8% more electrical energy. An even greater reduction in pump or fan efficiency can occur if the motor is lightly loaded and therefore operates even faster than its Full-Load RPM rating. Because of this sensitivity of centrifugal loads to changes in operating speed, an energy efficient motor may actually provide little energy savings in some circumstances. This is an important factor to consider when replacing a standard motor with an energy efficient model.

   The best solution to this problem is to optimize the pumps and fan for each motor. This can be done by changing the size of drive sheaves or pulleys, adjusting the size or design of fans, or modifying pumps by installing a smaller size impeller or machining the existing impeller to maintain the design head and flow with a higher speed. However, in some cases this is not practical due to cost.

Another approach is to specifically choose a replacement motor with an operating speed equal to, or less than that of the motor being replaced. There is considerable variation in operating speeds among both standard and energy efficient models, so it is often possible to find an energy efficient motor that meets your speed requirements, as indicated by F.L. RPM ratings. Since motor nameplate F.L. RPM ratings are usually rounded to the nearest 5 RPM, users should try to obtain actual engineering data on a specific motor when selecting and installing it in a centrifugal load application.

Figure 7-4   Motor Efficiency Versus Full-Load RPM Rating

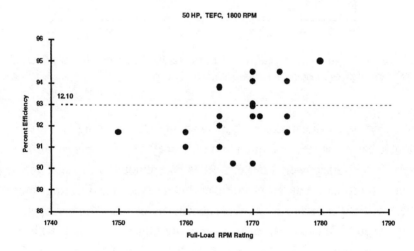

Energy efficient motors tend to operate faster than standard models, but this is by no means true in every case. The dashed line indicates NEMA 12-10 (93.0%) efficiency standard.

Figure 7-5   Operating Speeds Ranges and Averages
For Selected Motor Classes

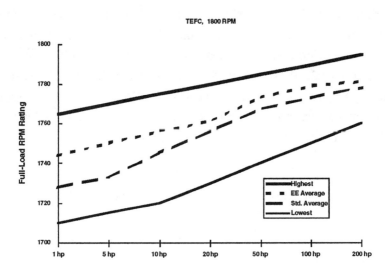

Energy efficient motors (meeting NEMA 12-10) have average Full-Load RPM ratings slightly higher than standard motors.

Example

Here is an illustration of how changing the operating speed of a motor can affect the operation and efficiency of a pump system. If a typical 50-horsepower, 1750 F.L. RPM pump motor with 100% loading is replaced by an energy efficient model, the actual savings may be less than expected if the replacement motor has a higher operating speed. Three replacement motors are considered, each with an efficiency rating of 94.3% (Table 7-4). Replacement Motor A has the same operating speed; there is no change in either flow or load so the full potential energy savings of 5.2% is achieved. Replacement Motor B has a full-load operating speed 15 RPM faster than the original. This increases flow by 0.9%. The motor's load increases by the third power $(1765/1750)^3 = 1.026$, an increase of 2.6%. Replacement Motor C increases the pump's flow by 1.7%, and load by $(1780/1750)^3 = 1.0523$, an increase of 5.2%.

Table 7-4   Flow and Load of Replacement Motors

	Efficiency	Operating Speed	Flow Change	Load Change	Input Energy	Demand Reduction
Original Motor	89.5%	1,750	0%	0%	42.6 kW	NA
Replacement A	94.3%	1,750	0%	0%	40.0 kW	2.6 kW
Replacement B	94.3%	1,765	+0.9%	+2.6%	41.0 kW	1.6 kW
Replacement C	94.3%	1,780	+1.7%	+5.2%	42.1 kW	0.5 kW

Three energy efficient replacement motors have the same efficiency rating, but a portion of the energy savings of models that operate at a higher speed will be converted into increased flow in pump and fan applications. Increased operating speed reduces the system's overall efficiency. This problem can be avoided in many situations by changing sheave sizes or pump impellers.

The increase in load must be subtracted from the efficient motors' energy savings. The actual energy savings of motors B and C depend on whether or not the faster motor's additional flow is captured by operating the motor fewer hours. In some situations an energy efficient motor provides no energy savings because of the increase in load.

Table 7-5   Energy Savings of Replacement Motors

	Savings with Load Capture	Savings without Load Capture
Replacement A	5.2% - 0% + 0% = 5.2%	5.2% - 0% = 5.2%
Replacement B	5.2% - 0.9% + 2.6% = 4.3%	5.2% - 2.6% = 2.6%
Replacement C	5.2% - 1.7% + 5.2% = 1.7%	5.2% - 5.2% = 0%

The actual savings of the energy efficient models that have a higher operating speed depends on whether the additional flow is "captured" for beneficial use. In an extreme case such as Replacement Motor C, the energy efficient motor provides no actual energy or dollar savings if the increased flow is not beneficial.

For this reason, replacement motors used for centrifugal load applications should be chosen with Full-Load RPM ratings equal to or less than that of the motors being replaced. In some cases a small increase in operating speeds may be acceptable if the replacement motor is significantly more efficient. For example, replacing a 1770 RPM standard motor with an 1775 RPM energy efficient model (a 0.3% speed increase) will increase flow by 0.3% and energy consumption by 0.9%. If this additional flow is useful (for example, it will fill up a tank more quickly) and the new motor is several percentage points more efficient, you may still achieve enough overall savings to justify the change. The newest version of MotorMaster software, described in Chapter 12, automatically incorporates motor operating speed in its savings analysis.

Are energy efficient motors available in slower speeds? The answer is usually yes, if you look for them. It is possible to find an energy efficient replacement motor with a Full-Load RPM rating low enough to replace most standard efficient motors, although you may have a limited choice.

For an actual example of typical Full-Load RPM ratings of commercially available motors, see Figure 7-6, which shows a MotorMaster software report for 50-horsepower, TEFC, 1800 RPM motors, ranked by full-load efficiency. Among models that meet NEMA 12-10 efficiency standard you can find one with a Full-Load RPM rating as low as 1765. Only four motors in the list have lower Full-Load RPM ratings. At the next higher operating speed rating (1770 RPM), you will find many choices, including six among the top ten most efficient. This is typical for other motor classes. Energy efficient models are available with operating speeds low enough to replace most standard efficient motors.

Figure 7-6   MotorMaster Software Report

11/28/93   **MotorMaster Database Query - Summary**   Page 1

CRITERIA: **Horsepower   ...   50**
Speed (RPM) ... 1800
Enclosure......... Totally Enclosed
Voltage .... 460 V
Features .... All Features

Manufacturer Modell		F.L. Eff.	F.L. P.F.	F.L. RPM	1/2 Load Efficiency	Catalog #	List Price
Baldor	SUPER-E	95.0	86.0	1780	95.0	EM4115T	3200
Reliance	XE TEFC	94.5	84.2	1774	95.1	P32G3346	3207
Marathon	BLUE CHIP XRI	94.5	85.0	1770	94.5	E210	3294
GE	ENERGY SAVER	94.1	86.5	1775	94.6	E967	2881
Toshiba	EQP III	94.1	84.2	1770	93.9	B0504FLF1USH	2881
Westinghou	OPTIM HE TEFC	94.1	88.0	1770	94.6	H05004TE	3053
Sterling	SILVER LINE	94.1	86.5	1770	92.4	JH0504FFA	3186
Magnetek	E-PLUS III	94.1	89.0	1770	95.8	E630	3381
Teco	MAX-E1/HE	94.1	86.0	1770	94.4		3467
US Motors	PREM. EFF. / TE	94.1	88.4	1775	95.1	A403	3467
Siemens	PREMIUM EFFICIENCY	94.1	82.9	1770	95.1	HPK5642	3467
Tatung	TH0504FFA	94.1	86.5	1770	92.4		n/a
Brook Crom	Argus - PE	93.8	86.0	1765	92.0	3224217PE	2066
Magnetek	E-PLUS	93.0	89.0	1770	93.6	E622	3043
NEMA	**** 12-10 STANDARD**	**93.0**					
Lincoln	LINCOLN PREM EF CI	92.9	88.9	1770	94.0	PDT504	3467
US Motors	HOSTILE DUTY / CT	92.4	88.5	1775	92.7	F212	2487
Magnetek	STD EFF	92.4	82.5	1765	92.4	N601	2506
US Motors	CORRO DUTY / TC	92.4	88.5	1770	92.7	F212CD	2633
Reliance	E-2000 TEFC	92.4	80.5	1771	93.0	P32G3151	2959
Westinghou	OPTIM SE TEFC	92.0	91.0	1765	92.4	S05004TE	2489
Baldor	TEFC-RIGID BASE	91.7	83.0	1760	n/a	M4115T	2174
GE	STD EFF	91.7	85.5	1775	91.0	S316	2487
Teco	STD EFF	91.7	90.5	1760	92.4		2487
Tatung	TB0504FFA	91.7	86.0	1750	90.2		n/a
Marathon	BLUE CHIP	91.0	82.5	1765	89.5	H445	2487
Toshiba	STD EFF	91.0	87.0	1760	90.9	B0504FLF1U	2487
Dayton	CAST IRON HAZ. LOC	91.0	n/a	1765	n/a	3N495	3322
Brook Crom	METRIC	91.0	85.0	1765	89.0	3627217	3834
Lincoln	LINCOLN HI-E CI T-	90.3	88.6	1775	90.2	DT504	1932
Delco/Linc	T LINE	90.3	88.6	1775	90.2	6U5100	1932
Reliance	TEFC	90.2	83.4	1767	89.1	P32G312	2487
Siemens	STANDARD EFFICIENC	90.2	88.5	1770	88.0	HTK5607	2487
Brook Crom	CAST IRON	89.5	86.0	1765	88.0	3224217C	2487

MotorMaster software reports rank motors by descending full-load efficiency and include Full-Load RPM ratings. Models meeting NEMA 12-10 are available with Full-Load RPM ratings from 1765 to 1780. Out of 14 models below this standard only 4 have F.L. RPM ratings below 1765 and so would not be easily replaced by an energy efficient model.

THE ECONOMIC VALUE OF ENERGY EFFICIENT MOTORS

Several factors determine how cost effective it will be to purchase an energy efficient motor rather than a standard model, or which of several energy efficient motors will be your best value. These include how many hours a year the motor operates, its load factor, your energy prices, how much efficiency you gain from an energy efficient model, and how much more it costs. Generally, your energy savings must repay the price premium within a few years for an energy efficient motor to be considered cost effective. In later chapters we will consider specific economic evaluation methods for calculating the cost effectiveness of specific energy saving investments such as energy efficient motors. For now, lets look at their value in typical applications.

To obtain maximum potential savings, try to select a motor among the most efficient available, rather than one that just meets a particular standard. An additional point or two of efficiency can mean substantial savings over the life of the motor. Figure 7-7 illustrates the much larger savings available from the most efficient motors in various motor classes compared with motors that just meet the standard.

Energy efficient motors tend to offer savings at all load levels. Figure 7-8 shows the load curves for standard and energy efficient motors which demonstrate that energy efficient motors tend to provide even greater savings under part-load operation. Figure 7-9 shows the dollar savings energy efficient motors offer at four load levels, which indicates that savings are significant even at low loads.

Electric motors and equipment operated by them give off heat that can contribute to cooling loads in air conditioned or refrigerated spaces. Even a 10-horsepower motor can add hundreds of dollars to annual cooling costs. If possible, motors and other heat producing equipment should not be located in air conditioned spaces. If this is not possible, using an energy efficient motor provides double savings by reducing energy consumption directly and by reducing cooling loads.

Figure 7-7   Annual Dollar Savings Over Standard Efficient Motor

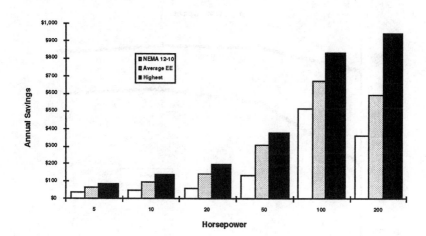

*This graph shows the annual savings of using various grades of energy efficient motors rather than a standard model. **12-10** represent motors that just meet the NEMA 12-10 standard. **Average EE** represents the average efficient of motors that exceed 12-10. **Highest** is the most efficient model in its class. By choosing one of the most efficient models available, your annual savings can be significantly higher than the savings offered by a motor that just meets NEMA 12-10. This calculation is based on 8,000 hours a year operation, $.04/kWh energy price, but the ratios would not change with different hours of use or energy prices.*

ENERGY EFFICIENT MOTOR PRICE PREMIUM

How much more expensive is an energy efficient motor? With careful shopping you may be able to find an energy efficient motor at little extra cost. Figure 7-10, is a scatter plot showing the relationship between efficiency and list price for a typical class of motor. Notice that motors with the same efficiency often have very different prices, while motors with the same price often have very different efficiencies. Since most motors are sold at a discount from list price, the relationships between individual motors may change slightly with respect to actual purchase prices, but the general pattern should be similar.

Figure 7-8   Average Efficiency of Standard and Energy Efficient Models

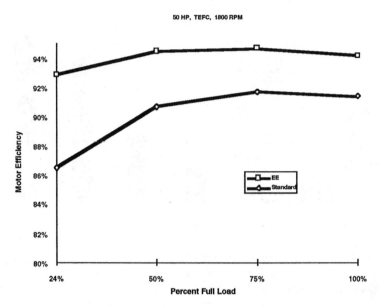

Energy efficient motors offer even greater efficiency gains when motors are operated with load factors below 60%.

Figure 7-9   Savings at Four Load Levels

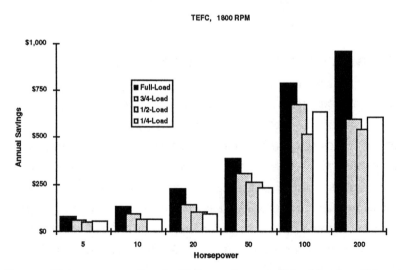

Energy efficient motors offer significant savings at all load levels. Although the total amount of electricity consumed goes down with reduced loads, energy efficient motors offer increased efficiency gains in low load ranges.

Figure 7-10   Motor Efficiency Versus Price

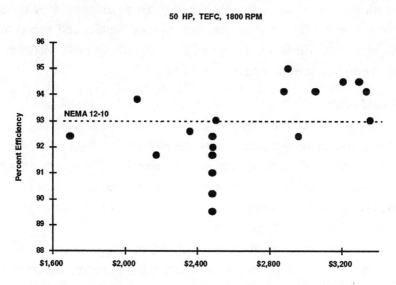

50 HP, TEFC, 1800 RPM

This scatter plot shows the relationship between full-load efficiency and list price for one motor class. Models toward the upper left show high efficiency and low price, while those in the lower right corner offer the least value. The dashed line indicates the NEMA 12-10 (93.0%) efficiency standard.

AVAILABILITY OF ENERGY EFFICIENT MOTORS

Energy efficient motors are produced by nearly all major motor manufacturers. However, in many regions where electricity prices are low, energy efficient motors are not well stocked by suppliers and may take a few days or even weeks to obtain. For this reason it is important to plan ahead to obtain an energy efficient motor. Motors are often selected based on quick delivery rather than efficiency, resulting in a missed opportunity to obtain significant long-term savings from a small additional cost.

To overcome this problem it may be appropriate to purchase an energy efficient replacement motor to keep as a spare, or better yet, install an energy efficient motor now and keep the old, standard model as a temporary backup. This can improve your motor system efficiency and reliability, and allows you to change the motor during scheduled downtime rather than during an emergency. Buying a motor before a failure gives you time to shop around and negotiate the best deal. Motor vendors often offer significant price discounts when you buy several motors at one time.

SUMMARY

Energy efficient motors are available from most manufacturers. Motors should be compared on actual efficiency ratings rather than model names that imply energy savings. Energy efficient motors are cost effective in many applications, and tend to offer benefits in addition to energy savings, including increased reliability, longer warranties and quieter operation.

Although there are some general differences between standard and energy efficient motors, they do not apply in every case so it is important to evaluate performance and purchase information of each model individually. Any new motor, no matter what the efficiency, should be selected to avoid problems with high inrush currents, insufficient locked-rotor torque, and increased operating speeds in centrifugal load applications. Potential problems can usually be avoided by proper energy efficient motor selection.

In later chapters we will see how you can obtain performance and price information on energy efficient motors, and develop a program for selecting the best motor for your application.

Chapter 8

Motor Controls

Controls are the brains behind a motor's brawn. A variety of control systems are now available that can increase the efficiency, performance, reliability and safety of motor systems. These controls are durable, accurate, small and quiet, and they can be installed with a variety of useful features. Most problems associated with earlier electronic controls systems have been overcome, and the technology continues to improve.

There are also potential pitfalls related to motor controllers. They can be expensive, often costing more than the motor they control, so it is important that they fit into your overall facility development plan. They must be correctly matched with other components to avoid straining your electrical system, conflicting with electrical protection devices, and damaging motors. Some controllers, especially inverter drives, can create power quality problems, so it is especially important that they be correctly selected and installed. Sophisticated controls must be correctly operated to achieve full potential benefits, which means training for your operating staff.

TYPES OF MOTOR CONTROLS

There are five general types of motor controls:

1. **Across-The-Line Starters.**

   These are basic manual on-off switches. They may also include operating lights, reversing, and various types of protection which shut down the motor if it becomes overloaded or overheated. Surge protection is also important to prevent damage from excess voltages created by lightening, capacitor switching, or a sudden insulation failure. Consult an electrical engineer to help design or troubleshoot your overload protection system.

2. **Duty cycle.**

   These automatically switch motors on and off as needed. For example, depending on the motor size and type, and the equipment it operates, it may be appropriate for a motor to be turned off when there is no load for more than a few seconds or minutes. Duty cycle controls can be as simple as a mechanical time clock, or they may involve sensors which send signals to a central computer that manages unit controllers (UCs) at each motor.

3. **Soft-start.**

   Three-phase motors typically draw six to eight times their normal operating current during the first few seconds of operation. Some design A energy efficient models draw even more. This high current draw can create a variety of problems. It can trip electrical protection devices, such as relays and fuses, or cause voltage drops, dimming lights and sometimes resetting electronic equipment such as computers and electronic controls. How much of a problem motor startup currents create depends on how robust your electrical power system is, and what other loads are on the motor circuit. Electrical distribution systems are often constrained by motor startup. Inrush current, and the heat it produces, can also place mechanical stress on the motor and the equipment it drives.

Several methods can be used to reduce inrush current. This is called **soft start**. Either manual or automatic controls are used to limit the power supplied to the motor for a brief period during startup. Soft starting is an important option to prevent voltage drop problems, and to accommodate growing electrical loads without expanding the electrical system capacity. It is especially important if a design A motor is installed. Soft-start techniques include:

- *Autotransformers and Primary-Reactor Transformers.* These reduce voltage, and thus current, to the motor. Auto-tranformers provide the most torque per ampere of any reduced voltage starter.
- *Primary Impedance.* A primary resistor or reactance can be applied in series on the motor power circuit to reduce current. The amount of current reduction depends on how much resistance is applied. In some cases, several steps of imped-ance are used to provide a smoother transition to full power.
- *Part-winding (also called "increment starters").* Motors with separate and isolatable windings can be connected so only half or two-thirds of the windings are engaged during starting.
- *Wye Start -Delta Run.* Motors capable of both Wye and Delta configurations can be connected in Wye during starting to limit current, then reconnected in Delta for full power operation.
- *Solid state controllers.* Various types of solid state soft-start controllers are now available that limit startup current. These starters often have additional features, such as overload pro-tection, diagnostic features to identify fault conditions, and dynamic braking.
- *Adjustable speed controllers.* Most adjustable speed controls have soft-start capabilities.

Figure 8-1   Soft Start Voltage, Current and Torque.

Soft-Start System	Voltage (Percent Full-Load)	Current (Percent Full-Load)	Torque (Percent Full-Load)
Full-Voltage	100%	100%	100%
Autotransformer, 80% tap	80%	64%*	64%
Autotransformer, 65% tap	65%	42%*	42%
Autotransformer, 50% tap	50%	25%*	25%
Primary-Reactor, 80% tap	80%	80%	64%
Primary-Reactor, 65% tap	65%	65%	42%
Primary-Reactor, 50% tap	50%	50%	25%
Primary-resistor, typical	80%	80%	64%
Part-winding, 1/2-start	100%	50%	50%
Part-winding, 1/2-start	100%	70%	50%
Part-winding, 2/3-start	100%	65%	42%
Wye Start-Delta Run	100%	33%	22%
Solid State/ASD	Various	Various	Various

* Autotransformer magnetizing current not included. This is usually less than 25% of motor F.L. current.

Soft starters vary in performance. Be sure to select a design that is suitable for each specific application.

An application's locked-rotor torque must be considered when selecting a soft-start system. Centrifugal load applications, which include most pumps and fans, have low locked-rotor torque requirements. Other applications may need careful analysis to determine which soft-start systems are appropriate.

4.   **Torque controls**

Some applications such as saws and grinders require constant speed but have varying torque requirements depending on how much they are loaded. A relatively new type of controller is now available that saves energy by reducing torque while maintaining constant motor speeds. Full power is restored within a few cycles when resistance is applied. Independent tests show that these controllers can save energy and operate reliably in certain applications. Manufacturers claim up to 40% energy savings depending on load and duty cycle.

5. **Speed controls.**

    Imagine driving a car with the throttle fixed at high and using the brake to control your speed. This would waste fuel, stress drive train components, and give you poor control. Of course, nobody would drive a car like that, but many motors operate pumps or fans at a fixed speed while their output is controlled by valves or dampers. A better approach is to control output by adjusting the motor's speed. According to studies by the U.S. Department of Energy, speed controls on pumps and fans offer the single greatest potential for electric motor system energy savings. Let's see how speed control saves energy.

Many motor driven applications have variable demand. For example, the flow needed in a water system or the amount of air needed to ventilate a building can vary considerably during a day, week, or year. These systems are designed for a "peak" demand (that is, the highest level expected) that may rarely or never occur. These motors often operate at full power, while output is controlled by a valve if liquid, or dampers if air. Thus our comparison with a driver who controls speed with the brake.

Energy savings can be significant with centrifugal load applications because energy input is proportional to the cube of the application's operating speed and flow. For example, a 25% reduction in fan speed that reduces air flow by 25%, reduces energy demand by 58%. This relationship between fan or pump speed and energy is one of the "Affinity Laws" that are important in fluid engineering.

FAN/AFFINITY LAWS

1. Flow varies *directly* with speed. If a fan's flow is measured in cubic feet per minute (CFM), the formula looks like this:

$$\frac{CFM_2}{CFM_1} = \frac{RPM_2}{RPM_1}$$

2. System pressure (P) varies with the *square* of speed.

$$\frac{P_2}{P_1} = \frac{(RPM_2)^2}{(RPM_1)^2}$$

3. Load (HP) varies with the *cube* of speed.

$$\frac{HP_2}{HP_1} = \frac{(RPM_2)^3}{(RPM_1)^3}$$

This exponential (cube) relationship only applies to the friction head, which is the portion of energy that actually creates a flow. It does not apply to the static head, the portion of energy used to maintain lift, or to fixed energy losses in the motor. Most of the energy going into a pump that lifts water several hundred feet may go to maintain the head, and will not be saved by reducing speed, even if flow is reduced. Savings can be significantly overstated if calculations are based on both friction and head curves on a high pressure system.

Figure 8-2 compares the relationships between load (flow) and input energy for throttle (using a valve or damper to restrict flow) and speed control in typical pump or fan applications. The energy required for speed control is much lower than for throttle control at

Figure 8-2   Typical Load/Power Curve for Throttle vs. Speed Control

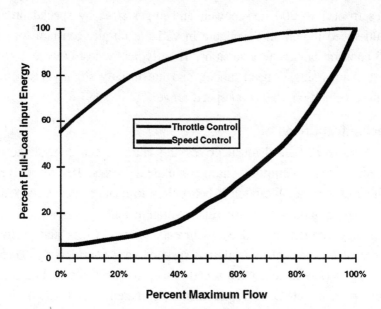

The upper line shows the energy consumption of a pump or fan system when flow is controlled by a throttle valve. The lower line shows energy consumption of the same system with a speed control. The difference between the two lines represents potential energy savings from installing an adjustable speed drive.

medium and low flow, indicating significant potential energy savings, often cutting energy consumption in half. Actual savings depend on the specific system design and load curve. Speed control can also reduce wear on your equipment, improve equipment performance and product quality, and can incorporate other features such as soft-starts and automatic controls.

SPEED CONTROL TECHNOLOGIES

There are several ways to control drive system output speeds:

Multi-Speed Motors

Multi-speed motors may be the best option for applications with load profiles that match the available speeds. Two-, three- or four-speed motors are commercially available in common NEMA frame sizes from 1 to 200 horsepower, and larger sizes by special order. Multi-speed motors are available in variable torque, constant torque and constant horsepower versions. They typically cost 60% to 100% more than a single speed model, and are usually slightly less efficient, especially in the lower speed range.

Mechanical Drives

A variety of mechanical drives and clutches can control motor speeds. These including changeable gear boxes, Reeves drives (which uses a variable pitch V-belt pulley to change speeds), wound rotor motor, motor-generator sets, hydraulic and hydrostatic drives, frequency converters, and eddy-current clutches. Costs and performance of mechanical transmission systems vary considerably. These drives generally have limited speed range, low efficiencies, and relatively high maintenance requirements compared with modern electronic controls.

DC Drives

In the past, DC motors were often used in applications that required precise speed control. DC power would be supplied either using inverters to convert AC power directly, or by a motor/generator set. However, DC motors are relatively expensive to purchase and operate so they are used less frequently now due to recent improvements in AC electronic Adjustable Speed Drives.

Electronic Adjustable Speed Drives (ASD)

Inverter ASDs electronically reform the 60 Hz sinusoidal AC cycle into different frequencies. Recent improvements in microelectronics have made inverter ASDs the most popular option for most commercial and industrial applications. ASD prices, equipment size, and potential problems have reduced considerably in recent years while capabilities expand, improving their paybacks and increasing the applications in which they can be used. AC motors with inverter

ASDs are now used in applications with critical speed and torque requirements that previously relied on DC drives, such as paper mills. Electronic speed controls are the best choice in most applications, especially if a wide speed range and precise control are needed.

There are three common types of ASDs: voltage source, current source, and pulse width modulation (PWM). Each has distinct characteristics, limitations, and power quality impacts. Voltage source is most appropriate for several motors that all need to operate at the same speed. Current source is most appropriate for larger size motors. PWM is the newest control technology. It is proving to be the best choice for most applications with motors under 500 horsepower.

Before selecting an ASD, design options should be reviewed by a mechanical engineer familiar with the specific process to identify additional factors that may require consideration or cheaper alternatives. Sometimes other modifications to the system can meet your needs at a lower cost. For example, if a pump always operates at part load, it may be oversized. Greater savings may be achieved by downsizing the entire pump system or installing a smaller impeller or a smaller, lower speed motor. For variable loads, a booster pump may be used to meet peak demands. ASDs may not save energy if a pump fills a reservoir or tank and cycles off. In such cases more energy may be saved by installing a small, optimally sized pump to operate continuously, with the main pump used as a backup.

It is important to consider all costs and options when selecting an ASD system. ASDs may require installation of new electrical protection devices. It could require purchase of a new motor designed for inverter application. Be sure to budget staff training time to insure that the equipment is properly operated and not abused. Since the drive itself produces some losses, efficiency is reduced when the motor operates at full-speed. To avoid this problem, the system can include a bypass circuit that powers the motor directly during full-speed operation. You may want to contact an independent electrical engineer for advice before selecting or installing ASDs. The system must be properly designed and installed to prevent potential problems. These include:

* **Power quality.** The high speed switching produced by inverters can create surges and other feedback in the power supply line, causing interactions with sensitive electronic equipment such as computers. In addition, ASD are themselves sensitive to power quality problems. If possible, ASDs should be connected to a dedicated circuit to minimize interference.

* **Motor stress.** Electric motors are designed to operate at a certain speed on standard, 60 Hz, sinusoidal power. ASDs reduce motors' operating efficiency by a small amount, which can increase internal temperatures, especially if the motor is operated with relatively high torque at slow speeds. Inverters also produce voltage spikes that stress motor insulation. Drive and motor manufacturers will often recommend specific models for use with inverter ASDs. MotorMaster software identifies motors designated for inverter use. Be sure to provide thermal protection and adequate air circulation. In some cases supplemental cooling is added to speed controlled motors to prevent overheating. Inductors installed between the motor and control can dampen voltage spikes, reducing stress on the motor insulation. Always consult the manufacturer before using a motor for inverter ASD applications.

* **Noise and vibration.** Harmonic resonances produced at certain frequencies by ASDs can physically damage motors and disturb nearby equipment or people. To avoid noise and vibration problems many newer ASD controls can be programmed to skip specific frequencies which produce harmonics, and manufacturers often specify particular motors or motor types that are less prone to mechanical problems. These are issues that should be discussed with your ASD vendor.

CALCULATING POTENTIAL SAVINGS

The following steps describe how to estimate the potential savings of installing speed controls in a particular centrifugal pump or fan with negligible static head that uses throttles, vanes or dampers to control flow.

1. **Perform a "Load Analysis."**

    A load analysis is a test of the input electrical energy (kW) consumed by a motor at each load point. To perform this test, attach a wattmeter or ammeter to the motor and calculate kilowatts while you throttle down the system to each load point. Create a graph that charts kW against flow.

2. **Develop a "Flow Profile" for**

    A flow profile is a graph of the proportion of full flow that equipment operates at over time, as shown in Figure 8-3. If you do not have instruments to record flow directly, you can use a recording powermeter based on the kW-load curve developed in

Figure 8-3   Load Curve Suitability for Adjustable Speed Drives

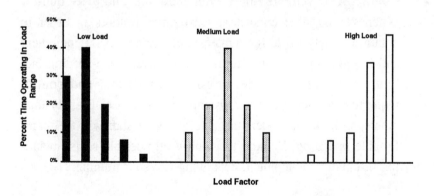

Low Load is a good candidate for ASD because it operates at a lower load factor most of the time. Medium Load is a fair candidate for ASD. High Load is a poor candidate for ASD because it usually operates close to full-load.

step #1. If the flow profile shows that the equipment is operating at less than 80% full-flow a significant portion of the time, it is probably a good candidate for speed control

3. **Estimate Energy Consumption**
   Calculate the estimated energy consumption using a speed control for each load level by assuming that energy savings are proportionate to the cube root of flow. As an example, reducing flow to 75% of full load should only require about 42% (.75 x .75 x .75) of full flow energy, if speed controls are used. Remember that speed control only saves energy on the friction head, not on the static head, so a careless analysis on a high pressure system can grossly overstate the benefits. Easy to use computer programs are available that automatically calculate speed control saving. Some of these are listed in Appendix I.

4. **Total Energy and Dollar Savings**
   Calculate potential energy savings for each load level in the flow curve, multiply times the amount of time the equipment operates at that level and sum the total. Multiply this times your energy rate to determine your potential savings.

5. **Contact ASD vendors for recommendations and price quotes.**
   Whenever possible contact at least three vendors in order to obtain a variety of design strategies and prices. ASD equipment and installation costs are determined by several site-specific factors, including ASD size, physical installation, and control requirements. Some control systems are more user friendly than others, so look for models that you and your staff will feel comfortable operating. Be sure to identify all possible costs, including installation, equipment, debugging and staff training.

6. **Contact your utility.**

Many utilities offer rebates on energy saving projects such as motor speed controls. You may find that a project which is not otherwise cost effective becomes quite attractive with a rebate. Utility staff may also be able to provide technical assistance in selecting ASD equipment and avoiding power quality problems.

Selecting, designing and installing a motor drive system is a specialty field that requires knowledge of constantly changing standards and products. If you are unsure about control system selection or design, contact an independent consultant or your utility energy conservation staff in addition to product vendors for advice.

BRAKING

Many motor applications require some sort of braking capacity. Several techniques are used:

- *Regeneration.* Motor becomes a generator, returning mechanical energy to the electrical system. This is the preferred option, minimizing stress on components and saving energy, but requires special control capability.
- *Mechanical brakes.* These can either be integral or added to the motor.
- *Dynamic braking.* Mechanical energy is converted to heat in resistors.
- *DC injection.* A direct current is applied across two phases of the AC motor. Mechanical energy is converted to heat in the rotor bars, which can place both mechanical and heat stress unless carefully controlled.

Braking requirements should be considered when selecting drives and motors. If braking is frequent consider regeneration as a way to save energy.

SUMMARY

There are many control options that can improve the efficiency and performance of your motor system. This field is constantly changing so it is important to obtain expert advice and contact a number of vendors to obtain current information and competitive prices. For more information obtain *Variable Speed Drive Fundamentals* by Clarence Phipps, also published by the Fairmont Press, or consult a drive and control system specialist.

Chapter 9

Preserving Efficiency in Motor Repairs

Each year more motors over 5 horsepower are repaired than are sold new. The quality of these repairs have a significant impact on the performance of motors in operation. This chapter provides information and recommendations to help you prevent motor failures, determine whether to repair or replace a failed motor, and obtain the best quality repairs.

WHY MOTORS FAIL

Under ideal conditions electric motors can operate for many years or even decades without failure. Motors fail for a number of reasons. About half of all failures can be classified as mechanical, often involving worn bearings or physical abuse. The other half result from some type of electrical problem, such as a short circuit where insulation has broken down. Contamination (by moisture, chemicals, dust or overgreasing) and thermal stress (caused by overloading or poor ventilation) often contribute to electrical failures. Moisture can accumulate when motors are not properly protected during shutdown periods. Only about 5% of motor failures are actually caused by old age.

When a motor fails you should try to determine the cause so that future problems can be avoided. Consider these questions:

- Could electrical, thermal or mechanical stress have contributed to the failure?
- Was the motor properly maintained, monitored and protected?
- Could a previous repair have contributed to an early failure?
- Is the motor the correct design for its application?

REPAIR OR REPLACE?

Imagine that you have an older car. The engine is causing you trouble. Your mechanic says the engine needs to be rebuilt. Should you do it? It would cost a lot of money, but is cheaper than buying a new car, making rebuilding an attractive option in the short run. On the other hand, it's possible that the mechanic won't be able to get the engine back to its original performance. Perhaps it's time to buy a newer car that gets better gas mileage and has other up-to-date features rather than sinking more money into your old one. These are important questions to consider before making your decision. Your motor repair decision deserves similar consideration.

It is usually cheaper in the short-term to repair rather than replace a failed motor, especially those over 50 horsepower. Repairing a motor is sometimes also quicker than obtaining a new one. Despite these short-term savings, always weigh possible long-term benefits from a new motor before deciding to have a motor repaired. Here are some things to keep in mind:

- Surveys indicate that many motors are improperly matched to their application. You may want to replace rather than repair a motor which is not optimal for its application, such as being too large, or designed for a different voltage or torque.

- In general, older motors are less efficient than new standard motors, and are considerably less efficient than new energy efficient models. This improvement in motor efficiency is especially significant in motors less than 100 horsepower. A failed motor can be an opportunity to move up to a more efficient model that saves money in the long run.

- Motors often lose efficiency during repair. Although under ideal conditions motors can be repaired back to their original performance, in practice repaired motors often lose a small amount of efficiency.

EFFECTS OF REWINDING ON MOTORS EFFICIENCY

It is difficult to predict with precision what efficiency a motor will have if it is repaired. In most cases the best you can hope for is that the motor will be returned to its original efficiency, as indicated on its nameplate. In practice, rewinding often results in reduced motor efficiency, especially compared with the performance of new, energy efficient motors.

Sometimes motor components are permanently damaged when they fail, such as from a short circuit that causes overheating, or a worn bearing that allows the rotor to rub against the stator, smearing the metal stator surface. Damage can also occur during the rewind process, when the stator is baked to burn out the old winding insulation. Temperatures over 350°C (650°F) can permanently damage insulation in the stator laminations, which increases core losses.

Core damage is not corrected during a conventional motor repair process. Core loss damage can be repaired by disassembling the core and relaminating with new insulation. However, this is a major job that is not performed by all motor repair shops, and is too expensive to be justified in most cases.

Since 1981, the Electric Apparatus Service Association (EASA) has recommended that repair shops install temperature controls on burnout ovens to prevent overheating. Because insulation gives off heat when it burns, a flame suppression system is required that sprays steam or water if the insulation ignites. Many shops do not have this expensive equipment, and sometimes it is bypassed to speed the rewind process. Motors that were rewound before 1981 or which are rewound in a shop that does not use burnout oven temperature controls may have significant permanent damage due to overheating.

Core losses represent about 25 percent of total motor losses at full load. The other 75 percent is made up of friction and windage, stator and rotor I^2R losses, and stray load losses. If a motor had a full-load efficiency of 90% (10% total losses), core losses represent about 2.5% of input energy (.10 times .25). If core losses increase by 40%, this represents approximately 1-point reduction in efficiency.

A variety of other factors can degrade efficiency during rewinds, as listed in Table 9-1. The wrong size wire might be used for rewinding. Errors or intentional changes in winding pattern can occur. Iron laminations can be shorted by machining clearance for a bent shaft or to clean up a damaged spot. Changes in bearing type is another common cause of reduced motor efficiency.

Table 9-1   Major Sources of Decreased Efficiency During Motor Repair

Action	Type of Efficiency Loss
Change in bearing type	Windage and Friction
Changes in fan type or size	Windage and Friction
Excessive burnout temperature (over 650°F)	Core Losses
Core lamination damage during winding removal or repair	Core Losses
Winding with smaller size wire	Stator I^2R
Changes in winding configuration	Stator I^2R /Stray load
Increased air gap	Stator I^2R
Degraded air gap symmetry	Rotor I^2R
Cracked or loose rotor bars	Rotor I^2R

This table summarizes the type of increased efficiency losses resulting from mistakes and damage that often occur during motor repairs.

There is no limit to the possible total degradation of motor performance. If efficiency is decreased by more than 5 or 10 percentage points the additional losses will often cause the motor to overheat if it is operated at full load, causing another failure. However, if operated at partial load, even an extremely inefficient motor can operate for years without failing.

TESTED EFFICIENCIES OF REPAIRED MOTORS

Tests performed by the Electrical Apparatus Service Association (EASA, the international professional organization for motor repair shops) have shown that new motors can be stripped and rewound to their original efficiency. However, testing of typical rewound motors indicate that in practice motors often lose efficiency and operate hotter after a rewind. An experiment by Ontario Hydro in the early 1990's involved purchasing and testing ten standard 20 horsepower motors, damaging the windings on nine (one was kept as a control), having them rewound at nine typical repair shops, and retesting. The results are shown in Table 9-2.

Table 9-2   Results of Ontario Hydro Motor Rewind Tests

	Original Average Efficiency	Post-Repair Average Efficiency	Difference
Full-Load	88.1%	87.0%	-1.1
3/4-Load	89.1%	88.2%	-0.9

These tests indicate that motor efficiency typically decreases when motors are rewound.

Eight of the nine rewound motors had increased stator line resistance. All nine of the motors were rewound with smaller size wire, which reduces efficiency. The average reduction in efficiency represents an increase in losses of 9%. The costs of these repairs ranged from $302 to $657, averaging $469. No correlation was found between price and the quality of work.

Taking into account the price of these repairs, the efficiency loss, and the cost of a new energy efficient motor, Ontario Hydro determined that paying $1,115 for a new motor with a 93.5% efficiency rating rather than rewinding would yield a simple payback of 0.7 to 1.0 years, based on continuous operation, $0.06/kWh and a $240 utility rebate. Without the rebate the payback still averaged an attractive 1.5 years. In other words, the loss in efficiency that commonly results from motor rewinds alone justifies the purchase of a new motor for applications operating long hours. Even a motor that only operates 4,500 hours a year would enjoy an acceptable 2- to 3-year simple payback.

In a study performed in the early 1980's by the General Electric Company, all makes of motors being repaired in their shop were core tested. The results indicated average core losses were 32 percent higher than expected. Dynamometer testing of 27 motors ranging from 3 to 150 horsepower which had been previously rewound showed total losses averaging 18 percent higher than motors that had not been rewound. An 18 percent increase in losses means a 1.5 to 2.5 percentage point decrease in full-load efficiency.

These and other experiments indicate that efficiency losses during motor rewinding typically average about 1 percentage point for motors less than 100 horsepower, and about 0.5 percentage point for larger motors. Since the efficiency of most motor models has improved significantly since the mid-1970s, an older, rewound motor is likely to be 2 to 4 points less efficient than current standard motors, and 5 to 10 points less efficient than current energy efficient models, depending on motor size.

EVALUATING MOTOR REPAIR VS. BUYING
A NEW ENERGY-EFFICIENT MOTOR

When a motor fails you have three options. You can have the motor repaired, buy a new standard motor, or buy a new energy efficient model. The difference in operating costs between these options can be substantial, as illustrated in Table 9-3.

Table 9-3 Operating Costs of New and Repaired Motors
(Based on 20 HP, 3/4-load, 8000 hours, 5¢/kWh.)

Option	Efficiency	Annual Operating Costs	Annual Savings Over Rewind
New, Energy Efficient	92.7	$4,828	$317
New, Standard Efficient	88.7	$5,046	$99
Standard Rewind	87.0	$5,145	$0

A new motor offers operating savings compared with rewinding your old motor. If you do buy a new motor, an energy efficient motor is almost always a cost effective investment.

The efficiency of the old motor is an important factor in determining the cost effectiveness of buying a new motor rather than repairing the old one. Although it is difficult to know what efficiency the motor will have after being repaired, you are probably safe to estimate that the efficiency of a rewound motor in the 25 to 150 horsepower range is about 1 point below its nameplate rating, or 4-6 points below the efficiency of comparable new energy efficient motors, depending on size. An even greater difference can be expected between old motors and new energy efficient models in sizes below 25 horsepower. Motors that were rewound before 1981 are likely to have lost efficiency due to overheating and probably have significantly lower efficiencies than new motor.

To determine whether a new motor is justified in a particular situation you can use the evaluation methods described in Chapter 11, MotorMaster software (also described in Chapter 11), or the simple guidelines described below.

MOTOR REPLACEMENT GUIDELINES

If you choose to replace rather than repair a failed motor, it is virtually always worthwhile to choose an energy efficient model rather than a standard model.

Replace rather than repair motors for any of these reasons:

- Motor is smaller than 30 horsepower.
- Repair costs 60% or more of a new motor purchase price.
- A new energy efficient motor is justified, as indicated in Table 9-4 or one of the analysis methods described in Chapter 11.
- Any factors indicate that the motor has experienced permanent damage.
- Motor was rewound prior to 1981.

Table 9-4   Motor Replacement vs. Repair Criteria

Energy Costs	Annual Hours of Operation
2¢ per kWh	6,000 hours
3¢ per kWh	4,000 hours
4¢ per kWh	3,000 hours
5¢ per kWh	2,000 hours

Choose a new energy efficient motor if your energy costs average the value on the left and the motor's annual operating hours equal or exceed the value on the right.

OBTAINING QUALITY REPAIRS

Motor repair is a demanding craft that requires experience, care, and the right tools. Most motor repair shop managers and staff are truly proud of their work, and desire to provide quality service. Many shops have quality control programs, provide staff training, and invest in the best tools and test equipment to insure consistent high quality results. This is good news for motor owners who want the best performance from their repaired motors. However, the skill, time and equipment to perform a quality repair adds costs, and motor shops are also under pressure from customers to minimize prices and turnaround time. The quality of your motor repairs therefore depends on finding a good motor repair shop and communicating your desire for optimal results.

When a motor fails you are usually in a hurry, so it is best to search now to find repair shops that you can trust. Motor shops tend to specialize in specific motor sizes and markets, so try to find one that is familiar with your needs. Choose shops that have suitable quality control and testing programs, and written quality assurance standards and procedures. Appendix E, *Motor Repair Shop Evaluation Forms*, provides guidelines for determining whether a particular shop has the essential tools and follows procedures for quality work.

About half of North American shops that specialize in industrial size motors are members of the Electrical Apparatus Service Association (EASA), a professional organization that promotes quality repair practices. EASA also provides its members with motor engineering data and advice, which can often help produce a better repair. Although EASA membership is one indication of a responsible repair shop, EASA repair standards are recommended, not enforced by the organization. It is therefore worthwhile to use additional guidelines to identify the best quality motor repair shop.

MOTOR REPAIR SHOP ESSENTIALS

Here are four critical features to look for when choosing a motor repair shop:

1. Micrometers and calipers accurate to four decimal places and calibrated within the last year, for precise bearing measurements.

2. Core loss testing always performed before and after stripping to identify damage caused by improper treatment.

3. Original wire size and winding pattern always duplicated.

4. Dynamic balancing performed on all rotors and armatures.

It is important to provide written instructions and specifications when you deliver a motor for repair. This guarantees that the motor repair shop understands the work that you want, and is especially useful if there is a disagreement over the work after the repair is completed. Appendix F, *Electric Motor Repair Specifications* provide a model that you can either copy or modify for your own use.

When a motor is delivered for repair, the shop should fill out a *Motor Repair Form*, such as Appendix G, that lists the perceived problems, the motor's operating environment, description of missing parts if any, past problems if known, the type of repair required, the urgency of the repair, cost constraints, and the person who should be contacted concerning the repair. As the work is performed, all checks and measurements, description of materials and parts used, winding patterns, notes about the repair, problems encountered, and final testing results should be recorded. See Appendix H, *Repairer's Quality Record* for an example form for recording this data. The shop should provide these documents to the customer upon completion of the job, and keep copies for their own future reference.

The motor delivered for repair should be visually inspected for cracks, broken welds and damaged or missing parts. Motor repair shops should use a core loss tester to screen motors prior to performing rewinds. This is a valuable step that quickly identifies motors with permanent damage to interlaminar insulation that should be replaced rather than repaired. Core loss tests should be performed when the motor is first disassembled, after burnout, and after rewinding to insure that losses have not increased. Exciting current and watts loss should be recorded for each test, and a physical check carried out to identify hot spots. Electrical tests, such as insulation resistance, hi-pot, and surge comparison should also be performed before the motor is repaired if the windings are still intact, and after the repair is complete. These test results should be compared with those of previous tests if available to identify possible problems. It is important that all tests be performed by trained staff and all instruments be calibrated regularly.

There are many steps in the rewind process all of which must be performed correctly to achieve optimal performance. A motor should be rewound with its original winding configuration. While a decrease in the number of turns in the stator winding reduces winding resistance, it also shifts the motor's peak efficiency point to a higher load factor, and increases its starting current. A reduction from 10 to 9 turns will increase a motor's starting current by 23%, which may overload your electrical distribution system.

The same or larger wire size should always be used in rewinds. If a repair shop uses a smaller diameter wire, stator I^2R losses will increase. Some older motors were built with aluminum windings, which should be replaced with copper. Also, the efficiency of some older U-Frame motors can be improved slightly by increasing the amount of copper in the slots. Machining the rotor can result in higher I^2R losses, reduced torque, and larger air gaps, and should only be performed under special conditions.

Repairs to a damaged core should be performed with caution since mistakes can easily reduce motor performance. In no case should a repair shop do such work without consulting the motor owner. Machining or grinding should be performed in such a way to insure that the laminations are cut cleanly and not burred over. Changes to the air gap should be avoided, and combined rotor and stator machining should never increase the air gap by more than 20%. In some cases, damage to interlaminar insulation can be repaired by inserting split mica, or completely dismantling and then restacking the stator, but this is an extreme and expensive approach. In most cases a motor with significant core damage should be replaced.

The best quality replacement parts should be used, including Class F or better insulation system. Windings must be carefully tied and blocked to ensure mechanical stability. Connections should be brazed rather than just crimped. The original size bearings should be

ELECTRICAL APPARATUS SERVICE ASSOCIATION (EASA) REWIND GUIDELINES

EASA offers the following guidelines to motor repair shops for maintaining efficiency during motor rewinds:

DO:

1. Conduct a stator core loss test *before* and *after* stripping.
2. Repair or replace defective laminations.
3. Calibrate all test equipment and measuring devices at least annually against standards traceable to the National Institute of Standards and Technology (NIST), the Canadian Standards Association (CSA), or equivalent standards laboratories.
4. Measure and record winding resistance and room temperature.
5. Measure and record no-load amps and voltage during the final test.
6. Have a quality assurance program.
7. Have and use, at a minimum, the following test equipment: ammeter, voltmeter, wattmeter, ohmmeter, megohmmeter, high potential tester.
8. Have a three-phase power supply for running motors at rated voltage.
9. Balance the rotor.

DON'T:

1. Heat stators above 650° F (350° C).
2. Sandblast the core iron.
3. Knurl, peen or paint bearing fits.
4. Use an open flame for stripping.
5. Grind the laminations or file the slots.
6. Increase the air gap.
7. Increase the resistance of the stator windings.
8. Make mechanical modifications without the customer's prior approval. This includes but is not limited to changing fans, types of bearings, shaft material, and seals.
9. Change the winding design.

From *Guidelines for Maintaining Motor Efficiency During Rebuilding,* EASA Tech Note #16, May 1992.

used, or a substitute selected based on the manufacturer's recommendations. Bearings should be uniformly heated to no more than 230° F with an induction heater, hot plate or oil bath, never a torch, to ease fitting onto the shaft. The rotor should be dynamic balanced to eliminate vibrations.

About 40% of shops surveyed in 1993 used burn out temperatures higher than recommended to prevent core damage. Be sure that your repair shop uses temperature controls during the burn out process to prevent heating over 650°F (350°C). This should include a temperature suppression system to cool the motor when winding insulation combustion produces heat. Some repair shops now use innovative techniques that do not involve baking to remove old windings. The winding ends are cut, then mechanically pulled through the stator. This method is preferred if you can find a repair shop that does it. Some repair shops may take short cuts in order to hurry the repair process or reduce costs, such as overheating the motor to speed the burnout process, using smaller diameter wire, reducing the number of winding turns, and failing to test motors for problems. These short cuts can reduce motor efficiency and reliability, costing more in the long run.

Bearings are usually replaced during rewinds and other motor repairs. Be sure that the new bearings installed are identical to the original. If bearings with non-contact seals are replaced by bearings which have rubbing seals, the motor's operating efficiency will decline due to increased friction. This is a common mistake made during motor rewinds and other repairs. Accurate bearing alignment is critical. Repair shops should have and used micrometers and calipers that are accurate to four decimal places and calibrated at least annually for precise bearing measurements.

When a motor is being repaired you should consider having temperature sensors installed in the windings, as described in Chapter 10. These are especially appropriate for large motors, critical motors, and motors that are not easily accessible for regular testing.

Motors that are rated as explosion-proof require special care. Repairs should only be performed by shops that are certified by Underwriters Laboratories, as specified in Standard 674. If the explosion-proof characteristics of a motor are not to be maintained, the nameplate must be altered to reflect this and the motor should never be used in hazardous areas.

"THERE'S A SUCKER BORN EVERY MINUTE"

Experienced engineers maintain a healthy skepticism toward claims of breakthrough techniques that improve the efficiency of existing motors, and with good reason. Such claims are usually false. In fact such techniques often reduce motor efficiency and increase costs.

One such method that appears under various names involves incorporating capacitors into the motor winding. This increases power factor, reducing input current (amps) but not significantly reducing energy consumption (watts), which is more difficult to measure. Although power factor correction is often useful, a capacitor located elsewhere in the motor circuit would achieve the same results, and capacitors outside the motor are much less expensive. A study by the Oregon State University for the Bonneville Power Administration concluded that this type of "High Efficiency" rewind reduces efficiency and cannot be recommended.

Some rewinders may claim to provide an "energy efficient rewind" that increases the efficiency of a standard motor. If the motor originally had inferior materials it may be possible to slightly increase efficiency by adding more copper. Although this option should be used whenever possible, the finished motor will never be as efficient as a new, energy efficient model since it lacks other design features that cannot be modified during the rewind process. In practice, the best you can usually hope for when having a motor rewound is that it will be as efficient as the nameplate indicates.

Another device is supposed to reduce motor energy consumption in home appliances such as refrigerators. It is a voltage controller that senses and controls the voltage to the appliance based on motor load. According to the manufacturers, inductive loads can operate with a lower voltage, which reduces power consumption. This may be true for some, but certainly not all, motors. Consumer Reports testing found that this device actually increased power requirements in the newer refrigerators they tested. Unless the electrical supply to a motor is at the high end of the allowable voltage range there is little or no potential savings.

Never rely on product vendors for estimates of energy savings. Check with an independent engineer or energy specialist before you spend money on unproven energy saving technologies.

SUMMARY

In many cases it may be cost effective to replace a failed motor with a new, energy efficient model, especially if the old motor is not the correct size or design for its application, or if the motor has been damaged by past rewinds.

Only have motors repaired at shops that demonstrate top quality work. Check that motor components are tested before and during the repair process to ensure that the motor can be brought back to its original efficiency. Repairs should be performed by skilled and careful staff, and quality materials should be used throughout.

When having a motor rewound specify that the repair shop use:

- Original winding configuration.
- Original or larger wire size.
- Class F insulation or better.
- Phase insulation between all phase junctions.

- Tie and blocking methods to ensure mechanical stability.
- Brazed rather than crimp connections.
- Correct lead wire and connection lugs.
- Core-loss testing before and after rewinding.

Replacement bearings installed during any motor repair should be identical in design to the original. Bearings with non-contact seals should not be replaced by bearings with rubbing seals. Precise alignment is essential for efficient and reliable motor repairs.

Chapter 10

Predictive and Preventive Maintenance

DEVELOPING YOUR P/PM PROGRAM

Motors are relatively undemanding. Good clean power, moderate ambient temperature, and a little lubrication is all they usually require in order to operate for years. This doesn't mean you should ignore your motors or defer maintenance, however, or you *will* have unexpected breakdowns. There are ways to identify potential problems in your motor systems long before they cause a failure. Your best strategy is to check your motors regularly, and maintain them carefully to avoid breakdowns and wasted energy. A predictive and preventive maintenance (P/PM) program can improve the efficiency and reliability of your motor system. You'll spend more time on scheduled work instead of dealing with emergencies. Your repair costs and unexpected down-time are reduced. A P/PM program puts you in control.

Typically, a dollar spent on P/PM yields two dollars in direct savings, plus priceless rewards from improved safety, better staff morale, and less worry. If you don't already have a P/PM program, consider starting one now. A P/PM program involves scheduling regular monitoring, maintenance and replacement of equipment. The program must be tailored to your facility's specific needs. It should cover your electrical distribution system, electrical protective devices, switchgear, motors, controls, transmission, and driven equipment.

Here are the major components of a motor system P/PM program:

1. Establish a predictive monitoring schedule. This may include daily, weekly, monthly, semi-annual, and annual routes over which data is collected and maintenance is performed. There are several types of monitoring that are described later in this chapter. Which monitoring equipment you use and how often you test depends on your facility needs, your experience, manufacturers' recommendations, your budget, and the guidelines provided here. Monitoring can be performed by your facility staff or contracted to a service company that specializes in this type of testing.

    You can copy the **Motor Inventory and Test Form** in Appendix D for recording motor test data, or create a form tailored to your own monitoring program. Better yet, develop a computer spreadsheet to record test results on a portable computer. Give every piece of equipment its own spreadsheet file, create a column heading for each type of data you collect, then add a new line each time you test the equipment. You can use the spreadsheet's graphing capabilities to view results, which will help identify trends as they develop.

2. Identify who is responsible for monitoring and maintaining each piece of equipment. Make sure that personnel are properly trained in safe operation, testing, and maintenance. Train and retrain.

3. Review test results regularly. This information will help you identify impending failures before they occur, and serve as a reference in the future.

4. Establish a record keeping system that includes operation, test and maintenance logs, maintenance schedules, manufacturers'

documentation, and repair reports for each piece of equipment in its own file. The files should be organized so that anybody can retrieve necessary data, even years later when all your current staff have left.

The National Fire Protection Association's Standard 70B, *Electrical Equipment Maintenance* provides guidelines on basic electric system and equipment maintenance review (note: information on obtaining this and other standards is provided in Appendix I-vi).

FREQUENCY OF MOTOR TESTING AND MAINTENANCE

The frequency of testing, maintenance, and overhauls for a specific motor depends on:

- Operating hours.
- Operating environment.
- Load condition.
- Frequency of starts, plugging, and reversals.
- Importance of operation.

Routine maintenance and inspection should be performed at least as often as recommended by the manufacturer, or according to guidelines in this chapter. Motors that operate under normal service conditions should be overhauled, on average, every five or six years if they run continuously, and less frequently if they operate fewer hours per year. Motors operating under severe conditions may need to be overhauled more frequently.

All equipment operating staff should be alert to the following indicators that a motor needs immediate attention:

- Unusually noisy operation.
- Increased vibration.
- Unusual electrical problems.
- Higher frame temperature.
- Slower acceleration when starting.

However, your P/PM should include more than the minimal procedures indicated in this standard. It may be worthwhile to consult a
specialist if you are uncertain about what data to collect, what testing
equipment to use, or what schedule to establish for your P/PM program. The specialist you consult may be an electrical engineer, a
mechanical engineer, or a motor repair expert depending on your
needs.

The goal of testing is to develop trend analysis. It is important to
test new or recently repaired equipment on short intervals to establish a baseline. Once relatively constant and predictable values are
recorded you can lengthen the intervals between tests. After you
have established baseline data, unexpected test results may indicate a
developing problem.

All instruments and tools should be checked regularly and calibrated to insure accuracy. Be sure that only qualified personnel carry
out motor inspection, testing, maintenance, and repairs. Learn, follow, and teach proper safety procedures and check that safety rules
are observed by staff. Motor circuits should be locked open at the
branch switch or circuit breaker whenever testing, maintenance, or
repair is done to a deenergized circuit. In addition to the electrician's
padlock, each switch should be marked with a tag indicating what
work is being performed, by whom, and for what time period. Be
sure to discharge any capacitors in a circuit that will be serviced.
Place warnings on equipment that may start automatically.

Safety First:

Learn, follow, and teach proper safety procedures and
check that safety rules are observed by staff. Before working
on or near motor-driven equipment, disconnect the power
source from the motor and accessories.

MOTOR SYSTEM TESTING AND MAINTENANCE

Here are motor system testing and maintenance activities to consider including in your P/PM program.

A. Electrical.

Caution

Be sure that motors are properly grounded. Improperly grounded motors can be dangerous.

As discussed in Chapter 5, your motor system will operate most efficiently if voltage, phase balance, power factor, frequency and harmonic levels are well within tolerances. Determine the optimum type and frequency of testing for your facility based on your own experience and the advice of an electrical system specialist.

It is important to have an electrical engineer review a facility's electrical distribution system after any major change to identify possible safety hazards, such as overloaded circuits, and power quality problems that reduce the efficiency and reliability of your motor systems.

If they don't already exist, create line drawings of your electrical system and a record system that identifies the type, capacity, manufacturer, and test cycle of all equipment. It may be useful to install special sockets at appropriate locations which allow electrical monitoring equipment to be easily connected to specific points within a circuit without shutting down equipment. Check with an electrical supply house or your instrument manufacturer to identify the best type of socket for your metering equipment.

Frequent electrical system analysis is especially important if you have inverter drives which can create harmonics and other power quality problems. Use only "true RMS" ammeters when reading drive system output power since harmonics, irregular wave shapes, and low power factors can give false readings on other instruments.

WHY SPECIFY "TRUE" RMS MEASUREMENTS FOR ASDS

Most Adjustable Speed Drives have at least six diodes for a full wave bridge rectifier that produces DC power. These diodes cause current harmonic distortion, primarily 5th, 7th, 11th, 13th, and so on. Depending on the amount of current for the control circuit, this distortion can be significant.

True Root Mean Squared (RMS) measurements include the current of these lower harmonics (the higher harmonics normally do not have much current magnitude since the impedance at the higher odd frequencies increases rapidly). Some instruments *average* and then sum the RMS measurements, which produce lower values then a *true* RMS measurement. True RMS measurement give higher and more accurate reading.

Measurements should be made on the drive's incoming lines, before the ASD.

The electrical system should be checked at least annually for power quality and mechanical problems such as loose connections and leaks to ground. All distribution circuit components should be physically checked, cleaned, and lubricated as needed in addition to electrical testing. Make sure that dust, dirt, and contaminants are kept off high-voltage lines and equipment to prevent unwanted circuit paths that can create dangerous and wasteful leaks to ground or short circuits. Electrical equipment and motors can be cleaned of dust and dirt using a vacuum or by blowing compressed air, using 30 psi maximum. Do not blow dirt or dust into electrical switches or protection devices, motor ventilating holes, bearings, or other delicate moving parts. Be sure that the compressed air does not carry water that may have condensed in the supply lines. Establish safety procedures to prevent accidents during cleaning activities.

Monitoring should include all switch gear, controls, and protective devices such as relays, circuit breakers, and fuses. This is critical since protective equipment may not function correctly if covered with cobwebs and dust, or if mechanical joints are contaminated or rusted. Look for loose pins and bolts, and frayed flexible leads. Test the operation of contacts and manual relays by hand, feeling for binding and sticking. Check contacts for pitting and signs of overheating such as discoloration, charred insulation, or odor. Contact resistance should be tested regularly on critical control equipment with a low-resistance ohmmeter. Readings should be about 50 microohms (50 millionths of an ohm). These test results should be recorded and tracked for trend analysis to identify contacts that may be developing problems.

Over-current testing should be performed on overload relays and circuit breakers to confirm that they operate reliably and to prevent moving parts from getting stiff. This typically involves disconnecting the component from the electrical system and applying three or four times the normal current rating to see that it performs as specified. Measure the time required for components to trip and compare measurements with the manufacturer's performance data. Test each pole of each circuit breaker separately. Test circuit breakers for instantaneous element pickup. This will verify that magnetic tripping occurs correctly. Many electrical problems begin with poor connections that heat, eventually causing failure. Follow manufacturers' recommendation for circuit breaker lubrication, and torque values for tightening terminals.

Several companies now provide various types of Motor Circuit Analysis, which involves use of specialized metering techniques that can identify a variety of problems.

MOTOR CIRCUIT ANALYSIS

Motor Circuit Analysis (MCA) includes a number of relatively new technologies used in portable electric motor circuit analyzers. The analyzer sends a series of low-voltage pulses around the circuit of a 3-phase AC motor. Problems such as leaks to ground and imbalances in inductance, capacitance, and resistance can be identified in a few minutes. Most test static (de-energized) circuits, although the newest technologies also test energized circuits and operating motors.

Operators have found that many motor problems originate in the circuitry. If identified in time, these malfunctions can be alleviated in most cases by "circuit grooming" (cleaning dirty connections, tightening loose ones, and replacing incompatible or worn components). If allowed to deteriorate, these circuit faults can create more serious problems that eventually damage motors, and even disable the entire circuit. MCA can also identify some problems within a motor. This testing is relatively inexpensive per motor, especially in a large facility where many motors can be tested in a few hours. Since MCA tests the entire motor circuit, it can identify more problems that if the motor is tested in a laboratory.

For more information contact:

CHAR Services Inc.
P.O. Box 119
Lebanon, PA 17042
(717) 273-8805   (717) 273-8931

CM Technologies Corporation (ECAD Division)
1026 4th Ave.
Coraopolis, PA 15108
(412) 262-0734; Fax (412) 262-2250

Liberty Technologies
555 North Lane
Conshohocken, PA 19428
Phone (800) 836-0330; Fax (215) 834-0346
(Provides testing of energized circuits).

PdMA Corporation
5909 Hampton Oaks Pkwy, #3
Tampa, FL 33610
(800) 476-6463; (813) 620-0206

Predictive Maintenance
114A S. 8th St.
Lyndon, WA 98264
(206) 354-3541

SAVO Electronics
P.O. Box 1373
Corvallis, OR 97339
Phone (503) 758-7235; Fax (503) 758-5610

B. Thermal

Operating temperature is an important indicator of motor performance and can alert you to many developing problems. A 10°C increase in motor operating temperature will typically reduce winding insulation life by 50%, and bearing lubrication life by 25% (Figure 10-1). Heat can originate from either the windings or bearings. An unexpected temperature increase may indicate an electrical or mechanical problem that reduces efficiency and could cause a failure, or that a motor needs to be cleaned.

Figure 10-1   Impact of Operating Temperature on Motor Insulation Life

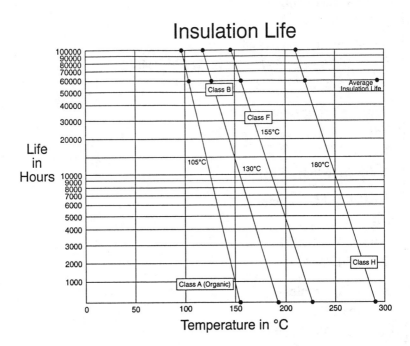

Insulation Life

Temperature in °C

Increased operating temperature greatly reduces motor winding insulation life.

It is a good practice for facility staff to place their hand on each operating motor that is easily accessible every day or two to feel for unusually high temperatures. Bearings temperature can be measured with a contact thermometer. A high temperature indicates that the bearing has probably failed and should be replaced before further damage occurs to the motor.

Many motors are built with automatic thermal protection that shuts off the motor if it gets too hot to prevent damage to the motor or a possible fire. Never bypass a protector due to nuisance tripping. Never install an automatic-reset thermal overload protected motor for an application in which the driven load can cause injury or damage if the motor should restart unexpectedly. Only manual-reset thermal overload protection should be used in such applications.

Winding temperature sensors can be specified for new motors or installed during a rewind. This typically costs a few hundred dollars extra. Although too expensive to be used in all motors, sensors are justified for large motors and critical motors, especially motors that are not easily accessible for other monitoring techniques. Type III sensors are relatively inexpensive but only indicate when temperatures exceed a set point. Type I and II sensors can also provide temperature readings for trend analysis. All of these sensors can be used to set off an alarm or automatic motor shut off when overtemperature occurs.

Infrared thermography is a relatively new technique that allows surface temperatures to be measured from a distance using portable scanners. This is an excellent way to identify some electrical equipment problems and hot bearings. These tests often pay for themselves in energy savings and increased reliability. Relatively inexpensive and simple hand-held scanners are useful for facility personnel to investigate suspected problems. Sophisticated recording thermographic cameras are used by professional services to review an entire facility and provide a report on problems, ranked by potential risk. A professional thermographic review of industrial facilities is recommended about once a year or after any major electrical system change.

INFRARED THERMOGRAPHY

All objects emit thermal radiation of a wave length depending on the object's temperature. Special infrared cameras can determine the exact temperature of an object, range from -20° to 400° Celsius, with up to 0.1° of accuracy, and record this information as a permanent picture (a thermograph). This technique can provide valuable information about the condition of electrical equipment including power lines, transformers, switch gear, motors, and drive gear.

Infrared thermography allows temperature measurements to be taken from a safe distance on operating equipment. Large areas can be scanned quickly and safely. Although hand-held infrared scanners are inexpensive and easy to use, they have limited capabilities. It is usually worthwhile to hire an infrared thermography specialist to scan an entire facility periodically. This usually takes from one hour to a full day, depending on facility size and complexity.

The specialist walks through the facility with a portable recording infrared camera while equipment in the facility is operating, following power lines and zooming in on junctions and equipment. Panels and enclosures are opened, and equipment is scanned from several sides if possible. An experienced operator can quickly identify potential problems including poor connections, leaks to ground, shorts, and bad bearings.

If a piece of equipment seems hot, the operator will often scan another similar unit to use as a reference. For example, two similar junctions or switches may be compared. This allows problem areas to be confirmed. Minor problems typically cause a temperature rise from 1° to 10° C, intermediate problems cause a 10° to 35° temperature rise, while increases over 35° usually indicate a serious problem in need of immediate repair. The worse the problem, the easier it is to identify.

After the session a report is assembled listing hotspots, especially those that seem to present a critical danger. All recorded images can be supplied with the report for documentation and future review. Facility engineers can use this information to schedule maintenance and repairs, and plan long-term electrical system improvements.

C. Vibration

As stated previously, facility staff should make a practice of placing their hand on each motor that is easily accessible every day or two to check for increased temperature or vibration. A stethoscope placed on a piece of equipment can help identify some mechanical problems, such as a failed bearing. New, extremely sensitive portable vibration analysis instruments can diagnose many more problems early and accurately. For example, it may be possible to identify whether a particular noise is caused by a bearing approaching the end of its operating life (high frequencies) or misalignment (frequencies one or two times the motor operating speed). This testing is especially effective if the operator has baseline reports showing the vibration "signature" of the equipment when operating properly. Recommended vibration testing intervals are specified in Table 10-1. It is increasingly common to install permanent vibration sensors on motors larger than 100 horsepower with alarms that provide a warning if problems are detected.

Table 10-1   Recommended Vibration Testing Frequency

Operating Conditions	1-Shift	2-Shifts	3-Shifts
Clean	Annual	6-Months	3-Months
Moderate	6-Months	3-Months	Monthly
Dirty	Monthly	Bi-Weekly	Weekly

This table provides recommended testing intervals for motors of standard importance. Testing frequency should increase for especially critical motors.

If a motor vibrates excessively during operation and no specific cause can be found, it may be poorly mounted. Check shims for looseness and gaps, and hold-down bolt tightness. Check the base for broken cement or welds, distortion or twisting that may affect alignment, and similar problems. Some bases are simply not strong enough to withstand the forces created by a motor, or they may have a natural vibration frequency that creates resonance at the motor's operating speed. In such cases the base may need to be reinforced or replaced.

D. Motor Windings/Insulation.

Winding insulation degradation is a common cause of motor problems. Insulation weaknesses can often be detected prior to failure using the following tests:

- **Insulation resistance (megohmmeter)**

  This is the simplest and most common insulation test. The motor frame is grounded and a 500- to 2,500-Volt DC potential is applied to the winding, typically for 60 seconds. A megohmmeter is used to measure resistance. A dry winding should yield readings of hundreds or thousands of megohms. A low reading indicates possible deterioration of windings or high moisture. IEEE standard 43 test criteria define minimum acceptable reading as 1 megohm plus 1 megohm per 1,000 Volts of motor voltage rating. Readings *must* be corrected for ambient temperature based on instrument manufacturers' instructions, or Figure 1 in *How To Get the Most from Your Electric Motors*, published by EASA (ordering information in Appendix I).

- **Dielectric absorption (polarization index)**

  This is an enhanced version of the standard Insulation Resistance tests, suitable for formed coil wound motors, which measures the change in resistance over time. The high-voltage DC potential is applied and resistance measured for 10 minutes. The ratio of 10-minute and 1-minute megohmmeter resistance readings are used to create a polarization index (PI). IEEE 43 test criteria prescribe minimum PI of 2.0 for formed coils with Class B or F insulation.

- **DC high-potential (Hi-pot)**

  An over voltage is applied gradually and in stepped increments to identify minute insulation weaknesses that might fail due to a voltage surge. In this test, leakage current (measured in microamperes) is plotted against applied voltage at each step. A straight line indicates winding integrity. A plot that curves upward indicates a winding that could fail at higher voltages, so the test should be discontinued at that point to prevent permanent damage to the windings. Because this test applies a high voltage to the insulation, it is important that it be performed carefully and infrequently to avoid causing damage. This test can cause premature failure of an operating motor which has weak insulation. For more information see Institute of Electrical and Electronic Engineers (IEEE) standards 112 and 432.

- **Surge comparison.**
  Surge testing is the newest insulation testing technique, and the only one not limited to identifying ground faults. This is useful since about 60% of insulation failures begin as turn-to-turn, coil-to-coil, or phase-to-phase which eventually develop into ground faults. Surge testing is based on the principal that each of the windings of a motor are identical. Brief, identical high-voltage, high-frequency pulses are applied across each combination of windings (A-B, A-C, B-C) and the responses are compared on an oscilloscope screen. If the windings are identical the images superimpose on each other and appear as a single trace. Two different traces indicate a problem. The nature of the problem can often be identified by the resulting pattern, which may include turn-to-turn, coil-to-coil, and phase to phase insulation defects. Surge testing requires special equipment that is more expensive than other tests.

Regular surge testing with occasional DC high-potential tests are the best combination for identifying potential problems. Tests are normally conducted at the load side of the motor controller, and require disconnecting any power factor correction capacitors. Both tests can usually be conducted in about 10 minutes. One large industrial facility tests their most critical motors every 6 to 8 weeks, less critical motors quarterly, and the least important motors every 6 months. This test schedule provides early identification of many motor winding insulation problems, allowing facility staff to reduce unexpected motor failures by 40%.

With any of these tests it's important to remember that resistance is affected by winding temperature. The resistance of a winding at operating (90°C) can be ten times greater than at ambient (40°C). Winding temperature should be recorded when making resistance tests, and results converted to a reference temperature. If a motor fails, it's previous winding test results should be made available to the motor repair shop to help technicians identify the type of repair needed.

E. Operating Speed and Load Factor

It is useful to take tachometer readings of motor speed on a regular basis to identify changes in load or other operating conditions such as temperature, voltage, and other power quality variables.

As described in Chapter 4, motor load analysis using a wattmeter should be performed on motors as part of your preventive maintenance and energy conservation program to insure that motors operate within their optimal and safe load range, and as an indicator of possible mechanical problems such as clogged filters or worn bearings. How often you test your motors, and how many samples you take each time, depends on the type of load the motor drives. A constant load may require only an occasional single test. Applications with variable or cyclic loads may need several tests to determine the normal range of loads. If possible, load factor should be measured when the motor is operating with various throughput, ambient temperature, operating pressure, and filter resistance to determine their impact on motor load.

Once the relationship between load (measured by a wattmeter) and operating speed (measured by tachometer) is known you can use changes in slip to indicate changes in load, if voltage and temperature are relatively constant. Review Chapter 4 for information on calculating slip.

METERING MOTOR OPERATION

There are several ways to record equipment operating hours, cycles and load. You may already have a portable meter or data-logger for spot checking motors, or you may want to have a run-time counter or recording meter permanently installed on some of your motors to maintain a continuous record. An inexpensive option specifically designed for this application is the Motor Logger produced by Pacific Science & Technology, Inc. When attached to the outside of the motor frame this small electronic device records running hours and cycles by sensing the electromagnetic field created when the motor is operating. It can be used on a motor either temporarily or permanently.

Another model produced by the same company, called the SmartLogger, also records time-of-use, total run times, and load profiles. This data is then downloaded into a computer for analysis using manufacturer-provided software. It shows on and off status in table or chart form, and can calculate operating costs based on your utility's rate schedule.

For more information on these and similar instruments contact:

MyTech Corporation
10125 Metropolitan Drive
Austin, TX 78758
Phone (512) 836-9400, Fax (512) 836-9548

Onset Computer Corporation
P.O. Box 3450
Pocasset, MA 02559-3450
Phone (508) 563-9000, Fax (508) 563-9477

Pacific Science & Technology
64 NW Franklin Avenue
Bend, OR 97701
Phone (503) 388-4774, Fax (503) 385-9333.

F. Ventilation and Cleaning.

Operating temperature has a significant effect on motor reliability and efficiency, so adequate cooling is critical. This means that motors should be kept clean and adequate ventilation provided. Dirt can foul lubrication and create a layer of thermal insulation that traps heat. Clean motors and switch equipment regularly. A vacuum, or dry compressed air (30 psi maximum) can be used to remove dirt. Avoid too much paint on the motor since extra layers of paint act as a thermal insulator, making the motor run hotter. Follow manufacturer's recommendations concerning painting.

G. Mechanical.

Check mounting bolts for tightness, steel base plates for possible warping, and concrete bases for cracking. If the motor can be disconnected from its load you should turn it by hand to check for smooth and easy rotation. Motor shafts should be checked for endplay. Consult the manufacturer or your motor repair shop to determine how much axial movement is acceptable. Either too much or too little endplay can indicate bearing or shaft problems.

Check the connection between the motor and driving equipment regularly. Shafts should be accurately aligned using two dial indicators or a laser tool. Use shims as required under the motor base for alignment. For direct-coupled applications, use a flexible coupling, if possible, but not as a substitute for good alignment practices.

Pulleys, sheaves, sprockets, and gears should be secured with little or no play, and should generally be mounted as close as possible to the motor bearing to minimize bearing load, and positioned so the inner edge is no closer to the bearing than the shoulder on the shaft.

Drive belt tension should be checked regularly. Correct belt tension is especially important in high-speed, high-torque and high-horsepower applications. Under-tension will waste energy and increase belt wear, while over-tensioning increases wear to belts and bearings. After installing new belts, check tension often during the first 24 to 48 hours of operation and re-tension as needed. Belt manufacturers can provide recommended tension values. Instruments are available for precise belt tension measurements. For general applications the best tension is typically the lowest at which the belt will not slip under load. Belt flutter or squeal during normal operation usually indicate inadequate belt tension.

Consider replacing V-belts with synchronous belts, which operate more efficiently and reduce maintenance costs. Coupling tightness should be within tolerances. Belts should not produce excessive noise when operating.

H. Lubrication.

Proper bearing lubrication is essential for reliable motor operation. A significant portion of motor failures result from improper lubrication. Injecting too much grease or the wrong type of lubrication is a common cause of problems. Motor and bearing manufacturers can supply recommendations for how often to lubricate based on the type of bearings, motor speed, operating environment, and type of motor. If possible, use modern, high-grade lubricants, which have longer life and improved performance, but only if recommended by bearing manufacturers.

Motors 10 horsepower or smaller are usually lubricated at the factory to operate for years under normal service conditions without re-lubrication. The seals on these bearings should never be removed. Larger motors should be lubricated on a schedule based on manufacturer's recommendations and operating conditions. If you have no other guidance, a good rule of thumb is to grease the bearings of a motor in typical conditions every 2,000 hours of operation.

Caution

Too much grease or the wrong type of lubrication can destroy bearings and motors. Follow manufacturer instructions carefully.

Generally, the smaller the bearing, the higher the speed, and the hotter the operation, the more frequent regreasing is needed. Extremely dirty or wet conditions also require more frequent lubrication. Vertical shaft motors require lubrication about twice as often as horizontal motors due to heavy bearing loads.

Never over-lubricate! Too much grease can actually increase bearing friction and heat,and work its way into the motor windings, damaging the insulation. When these over-lubricated bearings run hot, technicians may think they need even more lubrication, escalating the problem. Grease should never be forced through the bearing seals, which can damage them. This leaves a layer of grease in the bearing cavity that increases bearing wear and heat buildup. Do not change lubricants without checking that the old and new are compatible, or carefully flushing out all of the old. Some greases will melt and drain out of the bearing if mixed together.

Take every precaution to prevent contaminating lubrication. A small particle of dirt or dust can damage bearings. If the motor is equipped with a lubrication fitting, clean the fitting tip and inject with a grease gun. Use one or two strokes on motors with NEMA frames 215 and smaller, two to three strokes for NEMA frame sizes 254 through 365, and three to four strokes for larger frame motors. For motors that have grease drain plugs, remove the plug before injecting grease and run the motor for 10 to 30 minutes with the drain plug open to allow old and excess grease to escape. This is important because the grease will expand as it warms. Only after grease stops exiting should the drain plug be replaced. If hard soap-like deposits escape from the drain it may be necessary to flush the bearing with hot oil to clean it. Be sure to purge all oil out of the bearing with new grease before operating the motor.

I.   Storage and Handling.

Long periods between operation can be especially hard on motors because moisture can condense in the motor frame, leading to winding failures. Motors should be covered and protected during storage and

Table 10-2   Recommended Relubrication Intervals for Motors
With Grease Fittings

Annual Operating Hours	Operating Conditions	Horsepower Range	Lubrication Interval
Continuous (8,760)	High temperature or vibration	< 50	6 months
		50 to 150	3 months
Continuous	Normal	< 10	2 years
		10 to 40	1 year
		50 to 100	9 months
5000	Normal	< 10	5 years
		10 to 40	3 years
		50 to 100	1 year
Seasonal	Normal	All	1 year (beginning of season)

If no specific lubrication instructions are provided by the manufacturer, use this chart to determine motor lubrication intervals. (Courtesy of Leeson Electric Motors).

shipping. Medium and large motors that will be subject to intermittent, seasonal or backup duty should be built with internal heaters to drive off moisture, or a low DC voltage can be applied to one phase of the motor windings in order to keep the windings 5-10° C warmer than ambient temperature. If this is not possible, run the motor a few hours each week to prevent moisture buildup and to lubricate bearings. Totally-enclosed motors should be stored with their drain plug open to allow any condensed moisture to escape. Make sure that steam and water are not directed into open enclosure motors.

When a motor is idle the lubricant flows out of the bearings, allowing moisture to collect on the highly polished bearing surfaces. Deterioration can begin almost immediately. To avoid this, rotate the shaft of unused motors monthly to maintain a protective lubricant film between the bearing rolling elements and the raceway. Try to use grease fortified with rust inhibitors on bearings that may be subject to condensation. Ball and roller bearings can also be damaged if idle motors are subject to shock or vibration, which can create depressions in the bearing surface called "false brinelling". This can occur if motors are stored adjacent to operating equipment or when motors are transported. Motor shafts should be braced during transport to prevent this problem. Contact a motor repair shop if you need advice on how to do this correctly.

K. Scheduled Replacement

To inexperienced observers it may seem wrong to replace operating components such as drive belts before they break, but there are reasons to replace some parts on a regular schedule:

- Avoid unexpected failures. It is much cheaper to replace parts during scheduled downtime than in an emergency.

- Scheduled replacement allows all components to be accurately ordered and installed. When equipment fails unexpectedly it is often replaced with the first workable part, and its installation may be rushed, a sure recipe for more problems.

- A scheduled replacement is often an opportunity to install better, more efficient or reliable equipment. For example, new cogged belts are more reliable and efficient than standard V-belts.

SUMMARY

Predictive and preventive maintenance can improve motor system efficiency and reliability and is an important component of your drive system optimization program. Predictive maintenance uses a number of techniques to identify mechanical problems while they are developing. A P/PM program allows you to avoid many unexpected equipment failures and energy losses.

Your P/PM should be tailored to your specific needs. You must determine what types of testing to perform, what instruments to use, and how often to test each piece of equipment. Organize your testing and maintenance program into weekly, monthly, quarterly, and annual schedules, and plan them to require minimal staff time. Use test results for trend analysis. Keep records organized so your investment in data gathering is not lost due to staff turnover.

Some of the tests described here require expensive instruments which must be correctly calibrated and used to give accurate results. Some tests are potentially hazardous. Be sure that staff are properly trained and always observe safety procedures.

Chapter 11

Investment Analysis

Should you *always* buy the most efficient motor or control system? Not necessarily. Energy efficient motors and controllers are cost effective in many situations, but choosing the best value for your application requires conducting a financial analysis. This analysis must take into account the energy efficient equipment's price premium, how much efficiency you gain, how many hours the equipment operates each year, your electrical rates, and whether an energy saving investment provides other benefits such as improved reliability.

In this chapter we will look at ways to calculate the dollar value of energy savings and determine which investment is most profitable in a specific situation. These analysis techniques can help you determine whether an energy efficiency investment is worthwhile, and identify which of several purchase options is best. They will give you confidence that you are making the optimal choice, and may help you justify energy saving expenditures to your supervisor or business manager.

We consider four typical situations for analysis:

1. **New Motor Purchase**
   You are buying a new motor. The question is, Which one? Should you pay more to buy an energy efficient model, and if so, how much more? In this case the cost of an energy efficient

motor is its extra cost, or "price premium", over a standard
motor. Installation costs will be the same no matter which motor
you buy.

2. **Repair or Replace a Failed Motor**

   In this case you can repair the old motor, buy a new standard
   motor, or a new energy efficient model. Although repairing an
   old motor is usually cheapest in the short run, especially for
   motors 50 horsepower or larger, a new motor is likely to be
   more efficient and reliable, offering long term savings. Buying a
   new motor may allow you to obtain a more suitable model for
   your application than your current motor. No additional installation charge is incurred because the failed motor must be
   removed and reinstalled, unless the new motor requires mounting
   modifications.

3. **Replace an Operable Motor**

   Should you replace an inefficient working motor with a new,
   energy efficient model? It may be cost effective in order to save
   energy, increase reliability, and to obtain a motor optimized for
   your application. Since the old motor still works, the price premium includes the new motor's purchase price, plus installation
   costs, unless you already plan to remove the old motor for maintenance. The old, low efficiency motor can be kept as a spare or
   used in applications with minimal operating hours so its remain-
   ing value should be considered.

Replacing an operating standard efficient motor with an energy
efficient model may be justified if it meets one or more of these criteria:

- Motor operates continuously and energy prices are high.
- Motor is oversized and underloaded.
- Motor is unreliable and its failure would incur high downtime costs.
- Motor has been rewound several times or abused.
- Motor was built prior to 1950.
- A utility rebate is available to cover a portion of these costs.

4. **Install Motor Controls**

Motor applications with variable load factor or duty cycles may offer substantial savings from the installation of Adjustable Speed Drives (ASDs) or other control devices described in Chapter 8. In this case you will need to consider the price of the control system, its installation costs, and training for your operating staff. In some cases you will also need to purchase a new motor to match the ASD system. Despite these relatively high initial costs, ASDs often provide substantial benefits including significant energy savings, improved process control, soft start capability, and reduced mechanical stress on equipment, making them a cost effective investment.

CALCULATING ENERGY COSTS

Energy costs are a critical factor in evaluating an energy efficiency investment. Your company's business manager or accountant, or your utility representative can help you determine what energy rate to use in energy cost calculations. Also ask for estimates of anticipated energy price increases during the analysis period; increases of 2% to 4% above inflation are forecast by most experts. Your company should use standard values for all energy efficiency investment evaluations.

Electric rates range from less than 2¢ to more than 10¢ per kWh, and can vary by customer class, season, time of day, and volume of energy purchased during a month. Typical commercial and industrial electrical rate schedules (also called "tariffs") may include the following features:

1. **Basic** or **Hookup Charge.**

This is a small fixed amount per billing period that is independent of the quantity of electricity used. This charge covers the costs of servicing your account. Improving energy efficiency does not affect this charge since it is a fixed cost.

2. **Energy rate.**

   Energy is measured in kilowatt-hours (kWhs). This rate may change depending on time of day, season of year, and the quantity of monthly energy consumption. It is not unusual for off-peak, off-season energy rates to more than double during peak periods. For accurate calculations of motor operating costs you must determine how many hours the equipment operates during each rate period. If your energy rate has declining blocks you should use the lowest block rate that you pay each month, representing your marginal cost of energy.

3. **Capacity** or **Demand charge.**

   This charge is based on the maximum power consumption in any 15- or 30-minute period during the month, measured in kilowatts (kW). The rate may vary depending on the season. Some utilities have ratcheting demand charges, which means that the highest peak consumption over the last three- or six- or twelve-month period is used to calculate demand charges. Demand may represent a significant portion of your total bill. A motor incurs a demand charge only if it operates during the month's peak period.

4. **Power Factor Penalty** or **Reactive Power Charge.**

   Low power factor indicates that a facility is consuming a proportionally large share of reactive power, which increases utility costs. Utilities often charge a kVAR penalty if power factor falls below an established value, such as 90% or 95%. Although power factor charges are usually only a few percent of a facility's total electrical charges, they are often enough to justify corrective measures. If your facility pays a power factor charge, oversized motors are probably major contributors to this cost.

5. **Internal Electrical Distribution Costs.**

   You should consider the costs of supplying electricity within your facility, in addition to utility charges when analyzing efficiency investments. Efficiency improvements and power factor

---

TYPICAL UTILITY INDUSTRIAL RATE SCHEDULE

Basic monthly charge: $19.00 for three-phase service

Demand charge: $5.35 per kW per month for all demand over 50 kW.

Energy charge (cents per kWh):

October - March	April - September	
5.2156	4.9672	for the first 20,000 kWh per month
4.1820	3.9829	for the next 155,000 kWh per month
2.9695	2.8281	for all energy over 175,000 per month

---

correction will reduce distribution losses and can avoid overloading a circuit that is reaching its rated capacity. This may help you avoid the cost of rewiring, adding transformers, and replacing switch gear that would otherwise be required to accommodate growth. Savings depend on many factors, including the robustness of the existing system, how close to capacity the system is being operated, how much growth is anticipated, and the cost of installing more capacity.

Reduced cooling may be another potential cost reduction from motor system efficiency improvements. Motor system components give off heat that can contribute to cooling loads in air conditioned or refrigerated spaces. Even a 10-horsepower motor can add hundreds of dollars to annual cooling costs. If possible, motors should not operate in air conditioned spaces. If a motor must operate in an air conditioned space, increased efficiency counts twice: once for the motor and once for reduced cooling costs.

COST CALCULATION METHODS

There are several ways to calculate the operating cost of a particular motor, and determine the savings from an efficiency improvement. We will consider two methods. The Simple Method uses a single energy cost value. The Precise Method calculates each time block separately.

Efficiency values used in these formulas should be based on operating load factor. Use part-load efficiency values when appropriate. For example, if the motor will usually be operating with a 75% load factor, the 3/4-load efficiency rating should be used if available, rather than the full-load efficiency value. If loads fluctuate significantly you can either use an average load value, or perform a separate calculation for each load level. For example, if the motor operates 1,000 hours a year at 20% load, 2,000 hours a year at 40% load, 2,000 hours a year at 60% load, and 1,000 hours a year at 80% load, you can perform four different energy consumption calculations and sum the total to determine annual energy use and operating costs.

Simple Calculation of Energy Costs

The easiest way to analyze energy costs is to calculate an average energy rate by dividing the total cost of a typical monthly bill by the kWh consumption. This gives you a single value that incorporates all utility charges. With this value you can directly calculate a motor's operating cost using the following formula:

$$\text{Operating Costs(\$)} = hp \times \frac{L}{100} \times hrs \times 0.746 \times C \times \frac{100}{Eff.} \qquad (11\text{-}1)$$

<u>Where:</u>

hp   = Motor rated horsepower.
L   = Load factor (percent of full load).
hrs   = Annual operating hours.
0.746 = A conversion factor from horsepower to kW units.
C   = Average energy cost ($/kWh).
Eff. = Motor efficiency (in percent).

Example:

A 50-Horsepower motor operates 4,800 hours a year at 3/4-load, with a 3/4 load efficiency rating of 91.4 and an average energy rate of 5¢ / kWh. Here is the calculation:

Annual
Operating $= 50 \times (75/100) \times 4,800 \times 0.746 \times .05 \times (100/91.4) = \$7,346$
Costs

Simple Calculation of Motor Efficiency Savings

To calculate your savings from using an energy efficient motor rather than a standard model, use this formula:

$$\text{Savings (\$)} = hp \times \frac{L}{100} \times hrs \times 0.746 \times C \times \left(\frac{100}{E_{st}} - \frac{100}{E_{ee}} \right) \quad (11\text{-}2)$$

Where:
Savings = Value of energy efficient motor energy savings.
hp = Motor rated horsepower.
L = Load factor (percent of full load).
hrs = Annual operating hours.
0.746 = A conversion factor from horsepower to kW units.
C = Average energy cost ($/kWh).
E_{std} = Standard motor efficiency (percent).
E_{ee} = Energy efficient motor efficiency (percent).

Example:

Here is the value of energy savings if the motor described above was replaced with one rated at 94.2% efficient:

Annual Savings =
$50 \times (75/100) \times 4,800 \times 0.746 \times .05 \times [(100/91.4)-(100/94.2)] = \$218$

PRECISE METHOD

A simple average energy rate may mask specific components of your energy charges and fail to reflect the actual cost of operating a particular motor. For example, two motors in the same facility which operate the same number of annual hours could have very different electricity charges if one runs at night incurring only energy charges, while the other operates during the day, incurring both energy and demand charges. For a more precise operating cost estimate, develop a spreadsheet that calculates the motor's energy charges for each time period, taking into account daily and seasonal rate changes, declining rates, and power factor charges. You may want to perform both Simple and Precise analysis on a few typical investments to see if they produce similar results. If they do, you can feel more comfortable using the simpler method for estimates.

Precise Calculation of Motor Energy Consumption

The following formula calculates a motor's rate of energy demand:

$$\text{Demand (kW)} = \text{hp} \times \frac{L}{100} \times 0.746 \times \frac{100}{\text{Eff.}} \qquad (11\text{-}3)$$

Where:
Demand = Rate of electrical energy consumption, in kilowatts.
hp   = Motor rated horsepower.
L   = Load factor (percent of full load).
0.746   = A conversion factor from horsepower to kW units.
Eff.   = Motor efficiency.

Demand is comparable to the rate of water flowing from a spigot. A kW value tells you how much energy is being consumed at any moment. To determine total energy consumption, multiply demand by the hours of operation. To calculate motor operating costs, multiply the kW times each energy rate times the number of hours it operates at that rate. Most utility rates charge different amounts per kWh depending on the time of day, season of year, or quantity of energy purchased during the month. For simplicity, you can calculate energy savings for a full year based on your average annual kWh rate. For greater precision, calculate the motor's operation during each energy rate time block separately.

Example:

A 50-Horsepower motor operates at 3/4-load with an efficiency at that load point of 91.4.

The motor drives the air handling system for a commercial building in a hot climate. The motor runs 6 days a week, 25 days a month. During the summer it runs constantly, day and night. During spring and fall it operates 8 hours a day and 8 hours a night. In winter it only operates 8 hours a day. During the summer the company's total energy consumption places it in the third block rate; during the spring and autumn it is in the second block rate; and during the winter months it is in the first block rate. Here is the facility's electric rate structure:

Table 11-1   Electric Rate Structure

Block	Summer Day	Summer Night	Other Seasons (Day or Night)
First Block (0-20,000 kWh)	10¢	8¢	5¢
Second Block (20,000-175,000 kWh)	8¢	7¢	4¢
Third Block (175,000+ kWh)	6¢	5¢	3¢
Demand Charge	$8.35/kW	NA	$4.65/kW

The cost of electricity usually varies with season, time of day, and the facility's total monthly energy consumption. It is therefore important to identify the actual value for each increment of energy savings when performing investment analysis.

First calculate demand:

$$kW = 50 \times (75/100) \times 0.746 \times (100/91.4) = 30.6$$

Second, multiply energy demand times the number of hours the motor operates at each rate block, as shown in Table 11-2.

Table 11-2 Annual Energy Costs

Month	Day Hours	Day Rate	Day Hours x Rate x 30.6 kW	Night Hours	Night Rate	Night Hours x Rate 30.6 kW	Total Day & Night
January	200	$.05	$306	0	$.05	$0	$306
February	200	$.05	$306	0	$.05	$0	$306
March	200	$.04	$244.80	200	$.04	$244.80	$489.60
April	200	$.04	$244.80	200	$.04	$244.80	$489.60
May	200	$.04	$244.80	200	$.04	$244.80	$489.60
June	300	$.06	$550.80	300	$.05	$459	$1,009.80
July	300	$.06	$550.80	300	$.05	$459	$1,009.80
August	300	$.06	$550.80	300	$.05	$459	$1,009.80
September	200	$.04	$244.80	200	$.04	$244.80	$489.60
October	200	$.04	$244.80	200	$.04	$244.80	$489.60
November	200	$.04	$244.80	200	$.04	$244.80	$489.60
December	200	$.05	$306	0	$.05	$0	$306
Totals	2700		$4039.20	2100		$2845.80	**$6,885.00**

Once the motor's incremental energy costs and operating hours are determined for each time period, a computer spreadsheet quickly calculates total annual operating costs.

Third, calculate annual demand charges by multiplying the motor's demand times the demand charge for each month that the motor operates during the facility's period of peak demand. If your utility's rate for demand charges is constant during the year and the motor's operating schedule does not vary significantly from month to month, you can simply calculate the motor's demand charge for one month and multiply it times twelve to determine total annual demand costs. If your demand charge changes seasonally or the motor will only operate some months during the peak period (perhaps because the equipment it drives operates seasonally or only operates at night some months of the year), calculate the demand dollar savings only for the months that it operated during peak periods and sum to obtain your annual savings. It helps to use a spreadsheet, as shown in Table 11-3.

Table 11-3 Calculating Peak Demand Charges

Month	Operates During Peak Demand?	Demand Charge	Demand Charge x 30.6 kW
January	no	$.4.65/kW	$0
February	no	$4.65/kW	$0
March	yes	$4.65/kW	$142.29
April	yes	$4.65/kW	$142.29
May	yes	$4.65/kW	$142.29
June	yes	$8.35/kW	$255.51
July	yes	$8.35/kW	$255.51
August	yes	$8.35/kW	$255.51
September	yes	$4.65/kW	$142.29
October	yes	$4.65/kW	$142.29
November	yes	$4.65/kW	$142.29
December	no	$4.65/kW	$0
Totals			**$1,620.27**

A motor only incurs a demand charge if it operates during the facility's peak demand, typically the maximum 15 minute period of energy consumption during the month. Demand charges vary by season in some areas, as shown here.

Finally, total energy and demand charges. In this example the operating cost of the motor includes $6,885.00 in energy and $1,620.27 in demand charges, totaling $8,505.27, somewhat different than was calculated using the Simple Method. Power factor charges increase the operating cost of some motors. Contact your utility representative to determine whether your facility is being charged for low power factor and, if so, for help to determine this cost for a specific motor.

Precise Calculation of Energy Savings

In order to determine the value of savings from a more efficient motor you could perform calculations of operating costs for each model then subtract the difference, or use equation 11-4 to calculate the difference directly in order to save steps.

$$\text{Demand Difference (kW)} = hp \times \frac{L}{100} \times 0.746 \times \left(\frac{100}{E_{std}} - \frac{100}{E_{ee}}\right) \quad (11\text{-}4)$$

Where:

Demand Difference	= Energy efficient motor demand reduction.
hp	= Motor rated horsepower.
L	= Load factor (percent of full load).
0.746	= A conversion factor from horsepower to kW units.
E_{std}	= Standard motor efficiency (percent).
E_{ee}	= Energy efficient motor efficiency (percent).

This difference in demand can then be used to calculate the operating savings from an energy efficient motor for each rate block.

Example:

If the 91.4% efficient motor in the previous example is replaced with a 94.2% efficient model, the reduction in demand is:

$$\text{Demand Difference (kW)} =$$
$$50 \times (75/100) \times 0.746 \times [(100/91.4)-(100/94.2)] = 0.9 \text{ kW}$$

This difference is multiplied times the hours the motor operates at each rate for each month to calculate the value of energy savings:

Table 11-4   Annual Energy Savings

Month	Day Hours	Day Rate	Day Hours x Rate x 30.6 kW	Night Hours	Night Rate	Night Hours x Rate 30.6 kW	Total Day & Night
January	200	$.05	$9.00	0	$.05	$0	$9.00
February	200	$.05	$9.00	0	$.05	$0	$9.00
March	200	$.04	$7.20	200	$.04	$7.20	$14.40
April	200	$.04	$7.20	200	$.04	$7.20	$14.40
May	200	$.04	$7.20	200	$.04	$7.20	$14.40
June	300	$.06	$16.20	300	$.05	$13.50	$29.70
July	300	$.06	$16.20	300	$.05	$13.50	$29.70
August	300	$.06	$16.20	300	$.05	$13.50	$29.70
September	200	$.04	$7.20	200	$.04	$7.20	$14.40
October	200	$.04	$7.20	200	$.04	$7.20	$14.40
November	200	$.04	$7.20	200	$.04	$7.20	$14.40
December	200	$.05	$9.00	0	$.05	$0	$9.00
Totals	2700		$118.80	2100		$83.70	**$202.50**

This shows calculations of energy efficient motor savings.

The difference in demand is also multiplied times the demand charge for each month to calculate demand savings:

Table 11-5   Peak Demand Savings

Month	Operates During Peak Demand?	Demand Charge	Demand Charge x 30.6 kW
January	no	$.4.65/kW	$0
February	no	$4.65/kW	$0
March	yes	$4.65/kW	$4.18
April	yes	$4.65/kw	$4.18
May	yes	$4.65/kW	$4.18
June	yes	$8.35/kW	$7.52
July	yes	$8.35/kW	$7.52
August	yes	$8.35/kW	$7.52
September	yes	$4.65/kW	$4.18
October	yes	$4.65/kW	$4.18
November	yes	$4.65/kW	$4.18
December	no	$4.65/kW	$0
Totals			$47.64

This shows calculations of energy efficient motor demand savings.

Adding $202.50 in energy savings and $47.64 in demand savings gives a total annual savings of $250.14 for the energy efficient motor.

EVALUATING INVESTMENTS AGAINST SAVINGS

Now that you have calculated the potential dollar savings you can compare this with the extra cost of the energy efficiency measure. Energy conservation can be treated as an investment; equipment purchase costs are evaluated against future energy savings, similar to having placed money in a savings account to reap future interest. Below are common methods that can help you determine the best investment option.

Simple Payback

Simple payback is defined as the cost of your investment divided by its annual savings. Here is the simple payback calculation for a new motor purchase or repair, when you only need to pay a price premium to obtain an energy efficient model:

Simple Payback = Price Premium / Annual Savings   (11-5)

If a motor operates but you are considering replacing it with a more efficient motor or installing an adjustable speed drive for the sake of energy efficiency you need to compare the full price of the motor or controller, plus installation and staff training costs (for ASD investments) against your annual savings. Here is the equation for calculating simple payback when buying new equipment:

Simple Payback = (NE + I&T - SV) /Annual Savings   (11-6)

<u>Where:</u>
NE = New Equipment Purchase Price.
I&T = Installation and Staff Training Cost.
SV = Salvage Value (if any).

Simple payback is an easy-to-use approach for making investment decisions. The maximum simple payback allowed for an energy saving investment is usually determined as a company policy. If an energy conservation strategy will repay its initial cost within the specified maximum time period it is implemented. Generally, simple paybacks under two or three years are considered attractive, and simple paybacks up to 5 years may be acceptable depending on circumstances. The MotorMaster software program described in Chapter 12 automatically performs simple payback calculations as well as providing information on motor performance and price.

New Motor Purchase Example:

A standard 50 horsepower motor costs $1,500. An energy efficient model costs $1,800, for a price premium of $300. The standard motor will cost $8,500 a year to operate, while the energy efficient model does the same work for $8,250, saving $250 annually.

	Standard	Energy Efficient	Difference
Purchase Price	$1,500	$1,800	$300
Annual Operating Cost	$8,500	$8,250	$250

In this case, $300/$250 yields a 1.2 year simple payback, indicating an excellent investment.

Failed Motor Example:

A standard 50 horsepower motor fails. Repairing it will cost $800. Its future annual operating cost, taking into account a slight reduction in efficiency, is estimated to be $8,750. The price for a new, energy efficient motor is $1,800. This motor would cost $8,250 a year to operate.

	Standard	Energy Efficient	Difference
Purchase Price	$ 800	$1,800	$1,000
Annual Operating Cost	$8,750	$8,250	$ 500

In this case, $1,000/$500 yields a 2.0 year simple payback. This is a good investment.

Simple payback can also be used to determine the most cost effective choice among several energy conservation options. For example, if several energy efficient motors are being considered, each with a slightly different price and efficiency rating, you should select the one with the shortest simple payback.

Other Economic Evaluation Methods

Simple payback is a useful technique for initial evaluation of energy saving investments, and may be sufficient for many decisions, but in some situations it is *too* simple. Simple payback does not incorporate inflation, interest rates, tax rates, fluctuations in annual savings, or the equipment's durability. Many investment decisions require economic evaluation tools that can take these complicating factors into account.

TIME VALUE OF MONEY

An important factor not incorporated into simple payback is the time value of money. When your firm evaluates investments, the current value of revenue diminishes the longer into the future the savings will occur, based on the profits that the money could earn if it were invested elsewhere. If investments typically earn 15% interest, then any energy saving investment you propose must earn at least that amount in reduced future costs or the firm is losing potential profits. Future benefits are therefore depreciated at a rate that reflects typical interest rates. Assuming a 15% interest rate, $100 saved over each of the next three years is only worth $228.32 today ($86.96 for the first year, $75.61 for the second year, $65.75 for the third year), not a full $300.

Most companies have standard investment analysis techniques, such as those described in Table 10-6. Contact your business manager or accountant for directions on which evaluation method to use, and for your company's tax and interest rate values in order to be consistent with other investment analysis.

Table 10-6   Measures of Economic Investments

Measure	Definition	Interpretation
Simple Payback	Number of years until investment costs are recouped through the flow of benefits.	A short payback period means greater benefit and less risk. Businesses often establish a hurdle payback period that investments must meet.
First-Year Benefit	Benefits in the first year after an investment is made, divided by costs, expressed as a percent.	A higher ratio indicates greater benefit and less risk.
Net Present Value	Present-day value of benefits minus present-day value of costs.	NPV greater than zero means an investment is economically efficient. Investments can be ranked according to NPV.
Rate of Return	The discount rate at which NPV = 0.	Rate of return should exceed a pre-set hurdle rate.
Benefit-Cost Ratio	Present value of benefits divided by the present value of costs. Indicates dollars of benefit per dollar of cost.	A ratio greater than one an investment is worthwhile.

Energy saving expenditures should be treated as an investment that yields a stream of future financial benefits. A number of different economic analysis methods can be used to identify the best investment option. Learn to use the method that is most common in your company or industry for evaluating motor drive system efficiency improvements.

UTILITY REBATE PROGRAMS

Your electrical utility may offer cash rebates for the purchase of energy saving equipment such as energy efficient motors and ASDs. These rebate programs are an important part of efforts to improve industrial efficiency and reduce environmental impacts. A utility rebate can make the purchase of an energy efficient motor or other efficiency investments especially attractive.

Why should utilities help their customers improve efficiency and reduce electrical consumption? Electrical demand is growing in most parts of North America. If unchecked, utilities would incur huge costs to expand their generation and distribution systems. Utility planners and the public agencies that regulate them realize that everybody's power costs can be kept down and profits are highest when growth in electrical demand is minimized. Increased electrical efficiency also improves industrial competitiveness by reducing production costs. Growing concern over the environmental impacts of electricity production, including efforts to prevent air pollution and concerns over the biological hazards of electromagnetic fields, further justify energy efficiency investments.

Calculating Simple Payback with Utility Rebate

When analyzing investments, subtract the rebate from the investment cost. For new motor purchase evaluation use this equation:

Simple Payback = (Price Premium - Rebate) / Annual Savings   (11-7)

When replacing an operating motor or making other energy conservation investments use this equation:

Simple Payback = (NE + I&T - SV - UR) /Annual Savings   (11-8)

Where:
NE = New Equipment Purchase Price.
I&T = Installation and Training Costs.
SV = Salvage Value (if any).
UR = Utility Rebate (if any).

Example:
A standard 50 horsepower motor costs $8,750 a year to operate. The price for a new, energy efficient motor is $1,800. It would cost $8,250 a year to operate. Installing the new motor would is estimated to cost $300 in staff time. A $500 utility rebate is available.

	Existing, Standard	New, Energy Efficient	Difference
Purchase Price	$0	$1,800+$300-$500	$1,600
Annual Operating Cost	$8,750	$8,250	$500

In this case, $1,600/$500 yields a 3.2 year simple payback. Without the rebate the payback period increases to $2,100/$500 = 4.2 years. These paybacks are moderately attractive, but may be acceptable to a forward-thinking company, especially if the new motor offered other benefits, such as increased reliability.

Rebate program requirements, and the size of rebates offered for an energy efficient motor vary from one utility to another. Some rebates require considerable planning, paperwork and verification, making them unsuitable for emergency motor purchases. Some programs have such limited funding that rebates are only available for part of the utility's budget period. The better programs are simple and responsive. These allow the rebate application to be handled by motor vendors, requiring no delay and little extra effort by motor buyers. Anybody who purchases electric motors should be familiar with their utility's energy conservation programs. Contact your utility to find out what motor rebate programs exist, what programs may develop in the future, and what is required to participate.

SUMMARY

There are many ways to improve the efficiency of your motor system that require an investment in new equipment or staff time. The evaluation methods described in this chapter can help you determine which investments are worthwhile and offer the best value. You will need to work with your business manager or accountant to establish procedures that are consistent with your company's other investment analyses. Once this is established, the evaluation of any specific proposal is relatively easy. Simple payback calculations are the easiest method for evaluating energy saving investments. Computer spreadsheets let you perform more complex calculations quickly and easily. Using well planned and consistent fiscal procedures will give you confidence that your energy saving investment decisions are justified, and should help gain support for equipment upgrading projects from your business manager.

Chapter 12

Selecting Motors for Efficiency and Reliability

Now that you are familiar with design and operating characteristics that affect electric motor efficiency and reliability, you are ready to go shopping. This chapter reviews issues explained in previous chapters concerning proper motor selection, and provides suggestions for finding and buying the optimum motor for each application.

GENERAL MOTOR SELECTION GUIDELINES

Selecting an electric motor is an important responsibility. The motor you buy will consume many times its purchase price worth of electricity over its lifetime. In many applications, a motor failure can cost thousands of dollars in lost production and staff time, plus frustration and embarrassment. By planning ahead, developing a methodical selection process, and using the following guidelines you will be able to choose the best motor for each specific application.

- Determine operation requirements for the motors in your facility. Create a file for each motor and motor application. Record information on peak load, duty cycle, maximum torque, power quality, and operating environment. You can use the **Motor Inventory and Test Form** in Appendix D, or create your own format for recording this information.

• Evaluate your operating motors to determine which ones should be replaced by an energy efficient model, and which should be replaced with a different size or design. Some motors should be replaced during the next scheduled downtime, while others should be replaced the next time they fail.

• Write a comprehensive purchase specification when buying motors. A "spec" defines motor design and performance requirements, including minimum efficiency. This tells vendors exactly what type of motor you want when requesting bids.

• Comparison shop. Develop a list of motor vendors in your area to contact for bids when you need a new motor. Obtain MotorMaster software for comprehensive motor performance and price data. If you live in Canada, obtain a copy of the Power Smart High Efficiency Motor database from your utility.

• Insist that all motor performance and price quotes are made on the same basis. Use *nominal* efficiency values based on IEEE 112 - Method B tests in the United States, or the appropriate test for other countries.

• Compare motor performance based on the efficiency values closest to the motor's typical load factor. For example, use 1/2-load efficiency values when comparing models for an application in which the motor will usually operate with a 60% load factor.

• Use the methods described in Chapter 11 to identify when an energy saving investment is cost effective. Consult your business manager or accountant to determine what investment analysis technique and values to use for consistency with other company investment decisions.

IMPORTANCE OF CORRECT DESIGN

Make sure that each motor is correctly matched to the application. Operating characteristics such as duty cycle, load factor, operating speed, torque and voltage affect the efficiency and reliability of your motor. Review the following list of factors to consider when specifying a motor:

1. Select a motor that is designed for your application's load and duty cycle. Design A and B motors are suitable for low and medium locked-rotor torque, and long duty cycles. Applications with high torque or short duty cycles may require a design C or D motor. Consult a mechanical engineer or motor vendors for advice on selecting the most appropriate motor design for your situation.

2. Choose a motor that is the right size for the load. Oversized, underloaded motors operate inefficiently and cost more than necessary. Undersized motors operate inefficiently and fail prematurely. Motors should not operate with greater than their rated load for more than short periods of time, even if allowed by their service factor.

3. Choose the most efficient motor you find that meets your design and price criteria. Since many motors have efficiency ratings that exceed NEMA 12-10 standard, don't simply specify an "energy efficient" motor. For motors that operate 4,000 hours a year or more, the best choice is usually the lowest priced motor among the ten most efficient models.

4. When selecting a replacement motor for centrifugal pumps or fans, choose one with a F.L. RPM rating equal to or less than that of the original motor. Use MotorMaster software to identify models that meet your F.L. RPM requirements, or write it into your purchase specification when soliciting bids.

5. If a motor will operate on a 208-Volt electrical system, choose one that is rated for 200-Volts rather than a "tri-voltage" motor (labeled "208-230/460"). Although a tri-voltage motor might not immediately fail, it will never be as efficient or as reliable as a motor optimized for 200-Volts.

6. Specify appropriate enclosure and protection features. Choose an enclosed frame if a motor may be subjected to wet or dirty conditions. Consider having thermal sensors built into the motor to provide overtemperature protection and accurate winding temperature information, and internal space heaters to prevent condensation if a motor will sit unused for extended periods of time. Discuss these and other special features with a design engineer or motor vendor.

7. Specify motors that operate with Class B temperature rise (maximum 130° C at 40° C ambient) and Class F or higher insulation system. This creates a motor that is more reliable and durable.

8. Follow the manufacturer's recommendations when purchasing a motor for an inverter ASD. Inverter duty places unique mechanical and electrical strains on a motor. Since ASDs often offer significant energy savings, the efficiency of the motor becomes a secondary consideration to the proper operation of the drive control system.

DEVELOPING A MOTOR SPECIFICATION

Write down the performance and design specifications you want before contacting vendors about purchasing a new motor. They typically include:

Design Features	Performance Features
• Frame type and size.	• Horsepower and service factor.
• Frame mounting arrangement.	• Duty cycle.
• NEMA Design.	• Minimum efficiency and power factor.
• Enclosure type (drip-proof, enclosed or explosion proof).	• Minimum locked-rotor and breakdown torque.
• Thermal sensor/protection.	• Minimum service factor.
• Space heating.	• Maximum full-load speed rating.
• Ambient temperature over 40°C or altitude over 3,300 feet.	• Operating voltage and frequency.
• Inverter application.	• Temperature rise and insulation class.
• Special wiring or conduit box location.	• Maximum starting current.
• Special features, such as integral brakes or special shafts.	• Minimum stall time

These are factors to consider when selecting a motor for your application. You may have additional factors to add to this list.

Purchase instructions should also describe standards (such as NEMA and the NEC) that the motor must meet, what documentation should be provided, and how and when it will be delivered. Make your specifications comprehensive but avoid being overly restrictive, especially regarding non-critical features. For smaller motors, your "specs" will be used to identify the best motor from among various production models. For larger motors, it may be used by engineers to design and build a custom motor. A well written specification is essential if you will be asking for bids from several vendors. Figure 12-1 shows an example of a motor spec. You can copy and use the blank **Motor Purchase Specification Form**, Appendix C, or create your own.

Figure 12-1   Motor Specification Example

Motor Purchase Specification Form	
Design Features	
Frame type	*Horizontal*
Frame size.	*326T*
Frame mounting arrangement.	*Standard*
Enclosure type.	*TEFC*
Thermal protection.	*At least 2 winding thermostats*
Space heating.	*Required*
Ambient temp. over 40°C or altitude over 3,300 ft.	*No*
Special wiring or conduit box location.	*No*
Special features.	*None*
Performance Features	
Horsepower.	*50 hp*
Duty cycle.	*Continuous operation*
Minimum locked-rotor torque.	*270 lb-ft*
Minimum breakdown torque.	*390 lb-ft*
Minimum F.L. efficiency.	*94.2%*
Minimum part-load efficiencies.	*94.7% at 3/4-load; 94.2 at 1/2 load*
Minimum power factor.	*86% at full-load*
Minimum service factor.	*1.15*
Maximum full-load speed rating.	*1775 RPM*
Operating voltage and frequency.	*230 Volt, 60 Hz*
Insulation class and maximum temp. rise.	*Class F or better, 80°C*
Maximum starting current.	*580 Amps @ 230 Volts*
Inverter application.	*No*

This shows a typical motor "spec." You should develop a similar spec sheet each time you search for a replacement motor in order to avoid mistakes and confusion.

Of course, in addition to these specific design features you want a motor that is well built, reliable, and backed with excellent service. Are there significant differences in quality, reliability, and service between manufacturers that may justify choosing one brand over another even if it means paying more or accepting a less efficient motor? There may be. Some motor users prefer certain brands, but two different users seldom have the same preferences. By all means, seek the advice of your colleagues as to which brands they believe offer superior quality and service. Take such advice with a grain of salt, however, since their experience may not apply to your purchase decision. The motor industry is fluid with manufacturers constantly upgrading, reorganizing, merging, and subcontracting production. Although your colleague may have had good service from Manufacturer A's motors and a bad experience with Manufacturer B in the past, the relative quality of their products *today* may be reversed. Manufacturer B may now even be producing some of Manufacturer A's products. The pool of models to choose from is reduced if you limit your selection to just a few manufacturers.

THE ELECTRIC MOTOR RETAIL MARKET

It helps to be familiar with the motor retail market so you can find and negotiate the best deal when shopping for a motor. There are currently over a dozen major companies manufacturing and selling NEMA 1 to 500 horsepower induction motors. Some of these companies are relatively small and specialized while others produce a full range of motors and other products. Some manufactures produce all their motors in North America. Others produce all their motors abroad. Several sell a combination of domestic and imported products. Most motors under 200 horsepower are mass produced, while larger motors tend to be produced on order, and are often custom designed to meet a purchaser's requirements.

Figure 12-2   Electric Motor System (EMS) Commercial Distribution

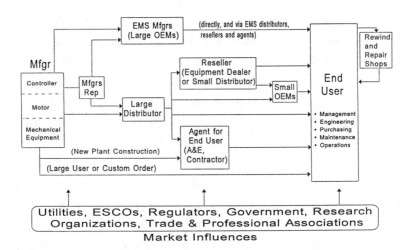

Motors and other electric motor system components are distributed in a number of ways. Some are sold directly from the manufacturer to users. Others are sold wholesale to large regional distributors or small local motor shops. Many motors are purchased in bulk and sold as original components of larger pieces of equipment. (Illustration from the *Electric Motor Systems Sourcebook,* courtesy of Resource Dynamics)

Motors follow a variety of paths from the manufacturer to the end user (Figure 12-2). Manufacturers often sell motors directly to large customers, such as original equipment manufacturers and large industrial companies that buy new motors by the dozen. Motors are also sold directly to large and medium customers through manufacturers' regional distributors. Customers making smaller orders buy their motors through motor retailers, who are usually also motor repair shops. These motor retailers may carry several brands of motors, although they usually emphasize one or two over the others due to the manufacturers' price structure.

Most motor manufacturers base wholesale prices on each dealer's annual sales volume of their products. For example, a dealer who sells less than $50,000 of a manufacturer's products annually may pay a wholesale price as high as 70% of list price. If that dealer sells $50,000 to $150,000 of the manufacturer's product, their wholesale price may go down to 60% of list price, while dealers who sell over $150,000 a year of a manufacturer's product may pay 50% or less. As a result, dealers may steer you to the brand that offers them the highest profit based on their wholesale cost, rather than the motor offering you the best performance.

The motor retail business is competitive, so dealers usually offer their customers discounts from the manufacturers' list prices, leaving minimal profit margins. Because of the market's wholesale price structure, a dealer who sells a large volume of a particular manufacturer's products may offer you significantly lower prices for the same motors than another dealer. Customers almost always receive a discount ranging from 20% to 50%, depending on how many motors they buy. Dealers often offer attractive deals if several motors are purchased at one time.

All of these factors emphasize the importance of planning ahead and comparison shopping for motors. A few minutes on the telephone or fax machine soliciting bids from several dealers may prove to be a cost effective investment of your time. If you obtain a significant discount for purchasing several motors at one time, you can use the opportunity to obtain energy efficient motors to keep in stock as backups, or to change out operating motors in order to save energy.

Although the motor retail business is competitive with narrow profit margins, especially for small shops, motor vendors are generally honest and responsible professionals who can provide invaluable advice and service. Don't be afraid to let them know your needs and ask advice.

OBTAINING MOTOR DATA

Your local motor shop can probably get a motor that meets your needs. It may even be in stock. But it may not offer the best combination of design, performance and price. The best motor may be one that is not sold by your regular motor shop. It may even be a brand that you have never heard of. It is essential that you obtain performance and price information from a large number of manufacturers to get the best motor value.

In theory you could request a catalog from every manufacturer listed in Table 12-1 and review them for motor performance and price data, but that approach is not very practical. For one thing, some manufacturers do not provide catalogs on request. And finding the information you need from catalogs is difficult and time consuming. Each manufacturer presents technical data in a different way. Some values must be converted to different units before you could compare motors. Many catalogs do not contain all of the performance information available.

Table 12-1   North American Motor Manufacturer Addresses

U.S.	**Canadian**
A.O. Smith 531 N. Fourth Tipp City, OH 45371 Phone: (513) 667-6800 Fax: (513) 667-5873	
Baldor P.O. Box 2400 Fort Smith, AR 72902 Phone: (501) 646-4711 Fax: (501) 648-5792	**Baldor** 522 Menton Court Mississauga, ON L5R 2Z6 Phone: (800) 521-4346 Fax: (315) 253-9923
Brook Crompton 3186 Kennicott Ave. Arlington Heights, IL 60004 Phone: (708) 253-5577 Fax: (708) 253-9880	**Brook Crompton** 264 Attwell Drive Rexdale, ON M9W 5B5 Phone: (416) 675-3844 Fax: (416) 675-6885
Dayton/Grainger 333 Knightsbridge Pky. Lincolnshire, IL 60069 Phone: (800) 323-0620 Phone: (708) 913-8333 Fax: (800) 722-3291	**Dayton/Grainger Canada** 24436 Van Born Rd. Dearborn Hts., MI 48125 Phone: (800) 633-8487 Fax: (313)295-3940

Motor Manufacturer Addresses (continued)

U.S.

Emerson Electric/U.S. Motors
8100 West Florissant Ave.
P.O. Box 3946
St. Louis, MO 63136
Phone: (314) 553-2000
Fax: (314) 553-1196

General Electric
P.O. Box 2222
Fort Wayne, IN 46801
Phone: (800) 626-2004
Phone: (219) 439-2000
Fax: (219) 439-4644

Leeson
2100 Washington Ave.
Grafton, WI 53024
Phone: (414) 377-8810
Fax: (414) 377-9025

Lincoln
22801 St. Clair Avenue
Cleveland, OH 44117-1199
Phone: (216) 481-8100
Fax: (216) 383-4730

MagneTek
1881 Pine Street
St. Louis, MO 63103
Phone: (800) 325-7344
Fax: (800) 468-2045

Marathon
P.O. Box 8003
Wausau, WI 54402
Phone: (715) 675-3311
Fax: (715) 675-6361

Reliance
24701 Euclid Ave.
Cleveland, OH 44117
Phone: (800) 245-4501
Phone: (216) 266-7000
Fax: (216) 266-7536

Canadian

Emerson Electric Canada
P.O. Box 150
Markham, ON   L3P 3J6
Phone: (905) 294-9340
Fax: (905) 475-4672

General Electric Canada
107 Park St. North
Peterborough, ON   K9J 7B5
Phone: (705) 748-7703
Fax: (800) 665-9329

Leeson Canada
320 Ambassador Drive
Mississauga, ON   L5T 2J3
Phone: (905) 670-4770
Fax: (905) 670-4378

Lincoln Electric of Canada
179 Wicksteed Avenue
Toronto, ON   M4G 2B9
Phone: (416) 421-2600
Fax: (416) 421-3065

Reliance Electric Limited
678 Erie Street
Stratford, ON   M4G 6W1
Phone: (519) 271-3630
Fax: (519) 271-8213

Motor Manufacturer Addresses (continued)

<u>**U.S.**</u>

Siemens
4620 Forest Ave.
Norwood, OH 45212
Phone: (513) 841-3100
Fax: (513) 841-3290

Sterling
16752 Armstrong Ave.
Irvine, CA 92714
Phone: (800) 654-6220
Fax: (714) 474-0543

Tatung
14381 Chambers Rd.
Tustin, CA 92680
Phone: (800) 828-8641
Fax: (714) 838-3295

Teco
6877 Wynnwood
Houston, TX 77008
Phone: (713) 864-5980
Fax: (713) 864-9502

Toshiba
13131 W. Little York Rd.
Houston, TX 77041
Phone: (800) 231-1412
Phone: (713) 466-0277
Fax: (713) 466-8773

Westinghouse Motors
IH-35 Westinghouse Road
P.O. Box 277
Round Rock, TX 78680
Phone: (512) 255-4141
Fax: (512) 244-5500

<u>**Canadian**</u>

Siemens Electric Ltd.
7300 Trans Canada Hwy
Point Claire, Quebec H9R 4R6
(514) 426-6064
(514) 426-6173

Teco Canadian Distributor
Madison Industrial
1970 Alberta St.
Vancouver, BC V5Y 3X4
Phone: (604) 872-8155
Fax: (604) 872-4563

Toshiba Canada
13211 Delf Place, Suite 610
Richmond, BC V6V 282
Phone: (800) 527-1204
Phone: (604) 244-2262

Westinghouse Canada
P.O. Box 2510, Station A
Hamilton, ON   L8N 3K2
Phone: (905) 528-8811
Fax: (905) 544-1781

A better way to obtain motor selection information is to use a computer software program called MotorMaster. It includes comprehensive performance and price data on thousands of motors covering most standard models sold in the U.S and Canada. You specify a horsepower, speed, enclosure type, and voltage range and the software provides a list of models meeting those criteria ranked by descending full-load efficiency. MotorMaster also calculates the energy and dollar savings of a particular energy efficient motor used in your application, taking into account all important variables including load, operating hours, purchase price, energy rate, and even a utility motor rebate if available.

MotorMaster includes considerable data on each motor as shown in Figures 12-3 and 12-4, including performance data such as service factor, efficiency and power factor, and purchase information such as list price and warranty duration. This information can be viewed on screen or you can print reports listing all motors in a specified class or providing comprehensive information on a particular model. There are several report formats to choose from. For example, if you need a motor that meets a minimum locked-rotor torque requirement, you can include that data field in the report. You can also identify models with special features such as vertical shafts, C-Face frames, 200-Volt ratings or U-Frames. The Power Smart High Efficiency Motor Database distributed free by Canadian utilities provides similar information on motor efficiency, but does not include other performance or price data.

Example:

You need a 50 horsepower, Design B, 1800 RPM, TEFC replacement motor for a centrifugal fan application. Reviewing the MotorMaster list for that motor class (Figure 12-4) you see that the Leeson Wattsaver model is one of the most efficient, with a F.L. rating of 95.0%, and relatively inexpensive, with a list price just over $3,000. However, if your fan operates primarily at 1/2-load, the

Figure 12-3   Individual Motor Report

11/29/93	**MotorMaster Database Query** - Single Motor			
CRITERIA:	**Horsepower**	50		
	Speed (RPM)	1800		
	Enclosure	Totally Enclosed		

Manufacturer:	Acme Motors			
Model:	Premium Efficiency			
Catalog:	3224217PE			
List Price ($):	2066			
	Full	**3/4**	**1/2**	**1/4**
Efficiency(%):	93.8	93.8	92.0	85.4
Power factor(%):	86.0	84.0	76.0	n/a
Full Load RPM:	1765			
Voltage Rating:	230/460			
Frame Size:	326T			
Features:	n/a			
Warranty (yrs):	2			
Service Factor:	1.15			
	FL	**BD**	**LR**	
Torque (ft-lb):	149	373	364	
	Idle	**FL**	**LR**	
Current (amps):	19.5	58.0	445	

This is a typical MotorMaster report for an individual motor. It provides performance and price information to help motor purchasers identify models that meet their needs.

Figure 12-4   MotorMaster Report of a Typical Motor Class

11/28/93   **MotorMaster Database Query** - Summary
CRITERIA: **Horsepower** **50**
                     Speed (RPM) **1800**
                     Enclosure ....   **Totally Enclosed**
                     Voltage ....   **460 V**
                     Features ....   **All Features**

Manufacturer Model		F.L. Eff.	F.L. P.F.	F.L. RPM	1/2 Load Efficiency	Catalog #	List Price
Baldor	SUPER-E	95.0	86.0	1780	95.0	EM4115T	3200
Baldor	INVERTER DRIVE, TE	95.0	86.0	1780	n/a	IDM4115T	4085
Leeson	WATTSAVER, CAST IR	95.0	87.0	1770	94.6	170023	3010
Reliance	XE TEFC	94.5	84.2	1774	95.1	P32G3346	3207
Marathon	BLUE CHIP XRI	94.5	85.0	1760	94.5	E210	3294
US Motors	AUTO DUTY / JDE	94.5	87.2	1780	94.1	E052	n/a
Lincoln	LINCOLN PREM EF U-	94.4	n/a	n/a	n/a	HQU504	3972
GE	ENERGY SAVER	94.1	86.5	1775	94.6	E967	2881
Toshiba	EQP III	94.1	84.2	1770	93.9	B0504FLF1USH	2881
Westinghou	OPTIM HE TEFC	94.1	88.0	1770	94.6	H05004TE	3053
Sterling	SILVER LINE	94.1	86.5	1770	92.4	JH0504FFA	3186
Magnetek	E-PLUS III	94.1	89.0	1770	95.8	E630	3381
Teco	MAX-E1/HE	94.1	86.0	1770	94.4		3467
US Motors	PREM. EFF. / TE	94.1	88.4	1775	95.1	A403	3467
Siemens	PREMIUM EFFICIENCY	94.1	82.9	1770	95.1	HPK5642	3467
Tatung	TH0504FFA	94.1	86.5	1770	92.4	n/a	
Brook Crom	Argus - PE	93.8	86.0	1765	92.0	3224217PE	2066
Magnetek	E-PLUS	93.0	89.0	1770	93.6	E622	3043
NEMA	**** 12-10 STANDARD**	**93.0**					
Lincoln	LINCOLN PREM EF CI	92.9	88.9	1770	94.0	PDT504	3467
US Motors	HOSTILE DUTY / CT	92.4	88.5	1775	92.7	F212	2487
Magnetek	STD EFF	92.4	82.5	1765	92.4	N601	2506
Reliance	E-2000 TEFC	92.4	80.5	1771	93.0	P32G3151	2959
Magnetek	U-FRAME	92.4	90.0	1765	90.2	U614	5064
Westinghou	OPTIM SE TEFC	92.0	91.0	1765	92.4	S05004TE	2489
Baldor	TEFC-RIGID BASE	91.7	83.0	1760	n/a	M4115T	2174
Sterling	K SERIES	91.7	83.5	1765	89.5	KB0504FFA	2234
GE	STD EFF	91.7	85.5	1775	91.0	S316	2487
Teco	STD EFF	91.7	90.5	1760	92.4		2487
Tatung	TB0504FFA	91.7	86.0	1750	90.2		n/a
Marathon	BLUE CHIP	91.0	82.5	1765	89.5	H445	2487
Toshiba	STD EFF	91.0	87.0	1760	90.9	B0504FLF1U	2487
Delco/Linc	T LINE	90.3	88.6	1775	90.2	6U5100	1932
Reliance	TEFC	90.2	83.4	1767	89.1	P32G312	2487
Siemens	STANDARD EFFICIENC	90.2	88.5	1770	88.0	HTK5607	2487
Brook Crom	CAST IRON	89.5	86.0	1765	88.0	3224217C	2487

A typical MotorMaster software report shows all motors in the selected class ranked by full-load efficiency. A variety of report formats can be selected by the user.

Baldor Super-E model offers a higher efficiency rating than the Wattsaver at that load point (95.0% vs. 94.6%), and its list price is only slightly higher.

Of course the list prices shown in a MotorMaster report are only a general indicator of the purchase price that you would pay for the motor, so you should contact the manufacturers or vendors of several models that meet your needs to obtain bids. In this case you might request price quotes for the six or ten top efficiency models. With firm bids you can perform precise payback calculations to identify which motor offers the best combination of price and performance.

If the motor you are replacing had a F.L. RPM rating of 1760, most of the top efficiency models, with F.L. RPM ratings of 1770 to 1780, would operate too fast. Unless you can adjust the fan's operating speed by changing the drive pulley size, increased operating speed would reduce your actual savings, as discussed in Chapter 7. You may want to limit your selection to motors with F.L. RPM ratings of 1760 or lower to avoid this problem, although you might consider a 5 RPM increase to 1765 if it offered a significantly more efficient motor. Your choice then might be the Marathon Blue Chip XRI, the most efficient motor with an operating speed of 1760. Although its efficiency rating is a little lower and its list price is a little higher than some others, it may offer the best combination of operating speed, efficiency, and price. MotorMaster will automatically incorporate increased operating speed into energy saving calculations of centrifugal load applications when calculating your operating costs and simple payback.

If the motor you are choosing will be used with an ASD, you might select the Baldor Inverter Drive model, which costs more but is designed to handle a drive system's extra stresses. You can even set MotorMaster to list only the motors that manufacturers have identified as being suitable for inverter drive operation. If your utility offers a rebate for energy efficient motors, MotorMaster can identify models that meet the program's minimum efficiency values, and can determine the size of the rebate you would receive.

Even if you cannot justify paying extra for an energy efficient motor, MotorMaster can often help you find the most efficient model in the standard efficiency price range. Using Figure 12-4 again as an example, you can see that the Brook Crompton Argus - PE with a full-load efficiency rating of 93.8% exceeds NEMA 12-10 yet has a list price of only $2,066, making it one of the least expensive models in that class. This shows the benefit of having performance and price information on the maximum number of models when shopping for motors.

MOTORMASTER PAYBACK ANALYSIS

MotorMaster computer software quickly calculates dollar savings and simple payback of using a more efficient motor, taking into account motor size, prices, efficiencies, annual hours of use, load factor, type of load (centrifugal or not), electricity costs, and utility rebates. It can be used for new motor purchases, rewind of a failed motor, or replacement of a working motor.

OBTAINING MOTORMASTER SOFTWARE

MotorMaster is an MS-DOS computer program that includes performance and price information on most commercially available NEMA design A and B motors in the 1 to 500 horsepower range sold in the U.S. It also performs simple payback calculations to identify when an energy efficient motor is a cost effective investment. It requires an IBM compatible computer with a hard disk and DOS 3.1 or higher.

MotorMaster was developed by the Washington State Energy Office (WSEO) with support from the U.S. Department of Energy and the Bonneville Power Administration. It is updated annually. MotorMaster can be purchased through the U.S. Department of Energy's Motor Challenge program described below. Registration costs $100 as of 1995. Copies are distributed free through some utility industrial energy conservation programs.

Figure 12-5

11/28/93 Motor Comparison and Payback Analysis Report		
Purchase of New Motor		
Model	**Standard Model**	**Energy efficient**
Manufacturer:	Acme Motors	Acme Motors
Model:	Standard	Premium Efficient
Enclosure:	Totally Enclosed	Totally Enclosed
Voltage:	230/460	230/460
Horsepower:	50	50
Speed:	1800	1800
Annual hours of use:	8000	8000
Percentage load:	75 %	75 %
Efficiency (%):	90.6 %	95.1 %
Dealer discount (%):	35.0 %	35%
Purchase price ($):	$ 1617	$ 2085
Motor rebate ($):		$ 0
Energy price ($/kWh):	$ 0.05	
Demand charge ($/kW-Mo):	$ 1.55	

ENERGY SAVINGS	**Standard**		**Energy efficient**	
	Model		**Model**	
Motor premium ($):			$ 468	
Energy use (kWh/yr):	247020		235331	
Energy cost ($/yr):	$ 12351		$ 11767	
Demand charge ($/yr):	$ 574		$ 547	
Annual energy savings:		11689 kWh	$ 584	
Demand savings:		18 kW	$ 27	
Total savings ($/yr):			$ 612	
Simple payback (yrs):			0.77	

This shows an example of a MotorMaster report comparing new standard and energy efficient models. After you select a specific model from the software's database and specify operating conditions such as annual hours of use, load factor and energy rate, MotorMaster automatically calculates operating costs, savings from the energy efficient model, and simple payback. Calculations can also be performed comparing a new motor purchase against repairing a damaged motor. This software makes it easy for you to identify the best investment option.

OBTAINING TECHNICAL INFORMATION ON ENERGY EFFICIENT MOTOR SYSTEMS

Due to the significant amounts of energy they use, motor systems are targeted by a number of agencies and utilities in their efforts to improve national and regional energy efficiency. These include:

U.S. Department of Energy Motor Challenge

The DOE sponsored **Motor Challenge** program is a joint effort by government, industrial motor users, motor manufacturers and distributors, designers, specifiers, and other key players to improve the efficiency of electric drive systems throughout the U.S. The ultimate goals of this program are to improve industrial competitiveness, increase energy efficiency, and enhance environmental quality.

The Motor Challenge Information Clearinghouse, managed by the Washington State Energy Office, provides publications, software, education and training materials, workshops, a computer bulletin board, and technical assistance to put information about energy efficient electric motor system technology into the hands of those who will use it.

Motor Challenge Partners are industrial motor users and other businesses that agree to collaborate with DOE to encourage increased use of energy efficient motor systems. Partners sign an agreement with DOE to incorporate energy efficiency as a necessary consideration in the design, purchase, and operation of electric motor systems, and to educate their employees about the benefits of energy efficient motor systems. Some Partners will participate in the Motor Challenge Showcase Demonstrations which will highlight specific examples of efficient motor system applications. All Motor Challenge Partners are recognized by the DOE for their leadership and cooperation toward increasing U.S. motor system efficiency.

Motor Challenge Information Clearinghouse
P.O. Box 43171, Olympia, WA 98504-3171
FAX: (206) 586-8303   Hotline: (800) 862-2086

The Hotline is staffed weekdays 6 a.m. to 5 p.m. Pacific Standard Time.

Electric Ideas Clearinghouse

The Electric Ideas Clearinghouse is a free information service sponsored by a coalition of federal agencies that is also managed by the Washington State Energy Office. It provides information on technical and policy issues, product availability, and training related to energy efficiency, conservation and management. It offers support for industrial energy efficiency technologies, including electric motor drive systems. The Clearinghouse sponsors a computer bulletin board which allows energy professionals to exchange information. The bulletin board has forums devoted to motor drive issues, as well as software that users can download for their own use. There is no charge for using this service, and callers in Western states can access it on toll-free lines. Callers from other regions must pay their telephone connection charges. To learn more about the Clearinghouse and its bulletin board call:

	Pacific Northwest	Other Western States	Other Regions
Voice	(800) 872-3568	(206) 956-2237	(206) 956-2237
Modem	(800) 762-3319	(800) 797-7584	(206) 586-6854
Fax	(800) 872-3882	(206) 586-8303	(206) 586-8303

Power Smart Motor Information

Most Canadian electrical utilities participate in the Power Smart energy conservation program, which offers substantial rebates for energy efficient motors. These rebates are based on a sliding scale that increases with motor size and efficiency. Power Smart utilities use and distribute a High Efficiency Motor Database in booklet form that lists models meeting their program requirements. Although the database does not provide performance data other than full-load efficiency, it does specify the rebate amount for each model. For more information, Canadian motor buyers should contact their utility's industrial energy conservation representative.

Energy Star Building Program

The U.S. Environmental Protection Agency sponsors the Energy Star Building program to encourage energy efficiency in commercial, industrial and public buildings. Businesses that participate in the Energy Star program receive information, support and recognition. Energy efficient motors and adjustable speed drives are a major part of this program. For information contact:

Energy Star Building Program
USEPA
401 M Street, S.W.
Washington DC 20460
(202) 233-9146

Utility Energy Conservation Program

An increasing number of electric utilities have demand side management (DSM) programs that provide technical assistance and sometimes loans or rebates for improving the efficiency of motor systems. These programs include a wide range of services and levels of support. For more information contact your utility's industrial representative.

Manufacturer Motor and Drive System Analysis Software

Some manufacturers supply their own energy efficient motor and ASD payback analysis software. These can be useful for evaluating the economics of an investment in energy efficient equipment. However, these do not replace the need for comprehensive performance and price data on different motors that can be obtained from MotorMaster software, or by obtaining bids from a number of vendors.

EASY ENERGY EFFICIENT MOTOR EVALUATION METHODS

You may find it helpful to have general energy efficient motor selection guidelines for use when you don't have the time or resources to perform payback calculations. Two simple methods for determining whether an energy efficient motor is a cost effective investment are described below. They are less precise than the economic analysis described in Chapter 11 or performed by MotorMaster software, but they may be sufficient for many situations.

Tables 12-2 and 12-3 can be used to determine whether a new energy efficient motor will meet common payback criteria. They are based on typical motor efficiencies and prices. Table 12-2 assumes that an energy efficient motor has a 15- to 25-percent price premium, that no utility rebate is available, and ignores other benefits of energy efficient motors. A lower price premium, a rebate program, or reliability benefits make energy efficient motors even more cost effective.

Table 12-2 Energy Efficient Motor Selection
(Minimum annual motor operating hours)

Maximum Simple Payback	Average Energy Rate			
	2¢/kWh	4¢/kWh	6¢/kWh	8¢/kWh
Two Year Payback	6,000	3,000	2,000	1,500
Three Year Payback	4,000	2,000	1,500	1,000
Four Year Payback	3,000	1,500	1,000	750

Choose a new 1-100 hp NEMA design A or B motor that meets the NEMA 12-10 standard if it will be used more than the specified number of annual hours for your average energy rate and maximum simple payback.

Example:

You are purchasing a new motor for an application which operates one shift (2,400 hours a year). Your marginal energy rate is approximately 4¢/kWh. Your manager requires energy saving investments to have a simple payback under 3 years. Should you purchase an energy efficient motor?

Yes. The cell at the intersection of **4¢/kWh** and **Three Year Payback** indicates that a motor must operate at least 2,000 hours a year to justify the extra cost of an energy efficient model. Your circumstances meet these criteria. However, if your manager requires a two year simple payback, you would not meet the requirements, so you should buy the most efficient motor in the standard motor price range.

Table 12-3 shows the dollar value of each point of efficiency gain for a motor that operates continuously (8,760 hours a year) at full-load for various motor sizes and energy costs. With this you can

Table 12-3   Annual Value of 1-Point of Motor Efficiency Gain
(Full-Load, Continuous Operation)

Horsepower	Energy Rate ($/kWh)							
	$0.02	$0.03	$0.04	$0.05	$0.06	$0.08	$0.10	$0.12
1	$1	$2	$3	$3	$4	$5	$7	$8
1.5	$2	$3	$4	$5	$6	$8	$10	$12
2	$3	$4	$5	$7	$8	$10	$13	$16
3	$4	$6	$8	$10	$12	$16	$20	$24
5	$7	$10	$13	$16	$20	$26	$33	$39
7.5	$10	$15	$20	$25	$29	$39	$49	$59
10	$13	$20	$26	$33	$39	$52	$65	$78
15	$20	$29	$39	$49	$59	$78	$98	$118
20	$26	$39	$52	$65	$78	$105	$131	$157
25	$33	$49	$65	$82	$98	$131	$163	$196
30	$39	$59	$78	$98	$118	$157	$196	$235
40	$52	$78	$105	$131	$157	$209	$261	$314
50	$65	$98	$131	$163	$196	$261	$327	$392
60	$78	$118	$157	$196	$235	$314	$392	$471
75	$98	$147	$196	$245	$294	$392	$490	$588
100	$131	$196	$261	$327	$392	$523	$653	$784
125	$163	$245	$327	$408	$490	$653	$817	$980
150	$196	$294	$392	$490	$588	$784	$980	$1,176
200	$261	$392	$523	$653	$784	$1,046	$1,307	$1,568

To calculate the annual value from an improvement in motor efficiency, multiply the value selected times the points of efficiency gain from an energy efficient motor, times the duty factor (percent of continuous operation), and load factor (percent of full load).

quickly calculate the annual dollar savings of an energy efficient motor by multiplying the appropriate value from the table times the points of efficiency gain from an energy efficient motor, times the duty factor (percent of continuous operation), and the load factor (percent of full load).

Example:

You are choosing a 50-horsepower motor for an application that operates two shifts (approximately 50% duty factor) at 75% load, with a marginal energy price of 4¢/kWh. A standard model has an efficiency rating of 91.4. The energy efficient motor has an efficiency of 94.2. To calculate, multiply $131 from the table, times 2.8 points of efficiency gain (94.2-91.4), times 50% duty factor, times 75% load for a total annual savings of $137.55. In this case you could afford to spend up to $275 extra for the more efficient motor and still meet a 2-year simple payback hurtle.

SUMMARY

Choosing the model that offers the best combination of performance, quality, and price can save energy and money, and improve the reliability of your motor system. There are several design features that you should consider, including load, torque, duty cycle, operating speed, voltage, operating environment, and protection. Discuss your application's operating conditions and other specifications with motor vendors or a mechanical engineer for advice on motor design features that will meet these requirements. Develop a purchase specification that describes the design features you want before soliciting bids to prevent confusion between you and vendors.

Finding and choosing motors among the many models available is easy if you use MotorMaster software, or the Power Smart database if you are in Canada. Obtain bids from as many vendors as possible. Choose the model offering the best efficiency and price value once you have identified motors that meet your needs. It is often possible to negotiate a significant price discount from your vendor, especially if you purchase several motors at once. With careful shopping you can usually gain efficiency at little or no extra price.

You can obtain free technical assistance on motor system design and motor selection from the Motor Challenge Clearinghouse or your electric utility's industrial energy conservation program. The key to obtaining the best motor is to plan ahead so you know what design features you need, where to obtain performance and price information, and how to determine when an energy efficient motor is worthwhile.

Chapter 13

Your Drive System Optimization Program

We have seen in previous chapters how planning, testing, preventive maintenance, and proper selection of replacement equipment are the keys to optimizing your motor system's efficiency and reliability. Now let's use this information to develop a drive system optimization program that meets the needs of your facility.

ESTABLISHING YOUR PROGRAM

To start, take stock of the condition of your motor systems, the information you have on each motor, your current testing procedures and tools, your decision making process for replacing and upgrading equipment, and your staff. Think about what you will need to follow through on the recommendations in this book. Write up a drive system optimization plan that includes:

- Comprehensive drive system review and testing.
- Identification of equipment to be upgraded.
- Selection of replacement equipment.
- An ongoing P/PM program to minimize equipment failures.
- Staff involvement and training.
- Data file organization.
- Investment analysis policy.

Depending on your existing resources, implementing this plan may mean slight modifications of current practices (if it doesn't require anything you can throw away this book because you are already doing everything right), or a complete overhaul of how your facility manages equipment. Most likely it will be somewhere in between. Include estimates of costs and benefits in your plan. You might also include goals, such as a specific reduction in energy consumption, equipment failures and downtime. Review the plan with your supervisor or business manager.

An energy management program needs support from the decision makers in your organization. Educate them about the benefits of energy management. Work with them to overcome problems and create institutional support for your efforts. If your proposal seems too expensive to them, try to negotiate a partial trial program.

Drive System Review and Testing.

With regard to your personal health, it's a good idea to have a complete physical checkup every year or two to identify early indications of problems and to serve as a baseline for future changes in your body. Similarly, your electrical system and drive equipment periodically deserve a good checkover. It may be appropriate to call in an electrical engineer to review your system, and work with you to determine an optimal testing and maintenance schedule. An expert can be especially helpful preventing power quality problems that may be created by inverter drives, electronic ballasts, and other electronic equipment.

Review the guidelines in Chapter 10 to develop your motor system testing schedule. At a minimum, tests should include voltage, amperage, load factor and mechanical conditions. If possible, tests should also cover power quality (harmonics, phase balance, and power factor), winding insulation, thermographic, and vibration analysis. Be sure to test at maximum load if the motor is subjected to load variations. You will need proper testing instruments that are regularly calibrated, and training for your staff to insure that testing is performed accurately and safely. If this is too expensive, consider hiring a specialty electronic testing service.

Identify Equipment to be Upgraded.

After all major drive system components have been tested, you can use your investment analysis policy to determine which should be upgraded to energy efficient models, and when. Divide your motors (and any other equipment if appropriate) into three categories:

1. *Motors offering rapid payback through energy savings, improved reliability, or utility rebates.* This typically includes motors which run long hours (more than 4,000 annual hours of operation), are currently inefficient (including oversized motors), have high reliability requirements, or are covered by attractive utility rebate programs. Use MotorMaster software or other sources of information to identify the most efficient and cost effective model that meets your needs. Order a replacement motor soon and install it at the next available opportunity, such as during a scheduled outage.

2. *Motors with an intermediate payback.* When these motors fail replace them with an energy efficient model. In most facilities the majority of motors fall into this category. Now is the time to contact dealers to review the efficiency and prices of available motors. After identifying the most cost effective replacement model you must decide whether to purchase it now, to keep on hand as a spare, or wait until the existing motor fails. This choice depends on how quickly an energy efficient motor can be obtained through suppliers, how quickly a failed motor must be replaced, and how many motors of the same size and type are used in your facility.

3. *Motors with extended paybacks.* These motors are already reasonably efficient, or are used only a few hours each year. They can be rewound or replaced with a similar motor.

It is important that the classification of each motor be clearly indicated to maintenance and repair staff. In addition to making a notation in the motor's file, you should establish some sort of marking system on the motor itself. For example, paint a red dot on the conduit box of all motors due for upgrading, and make sure that all staff know what this means.

Keep in mind that motors and other drive components have a long useful lifetime. The cost of running a motor may increase significantly in the future. Energy efficiency improvements that are not justified today may become worthwhile in a few years, so periodically reevaluate paybacks and reliability considerations.

Also look for potential applications of improved controls while surveying your drive system. Common candidates include pumps and fans that frequently operate with load factors below 80%, and motors that cause voltage drops when they start, in which case a soft-starter can reduce stress to the electrical system.

Selection of Replacement Equipment.

Imagine that one of the motors in your facility just broke down. What do you do? When a motor fails your foremost concern is to find a replacement as quickly as possible in order to get your equipment back into operation. Long term costs, including motor system efficiency, are a lower priority. The worst time to choose a motor is during a crisis, so don't wait for a failure. Now is the time to develop a replacement plan for each critical motor under your command.

Identify the size and type of motor you would need for each application in your facility. Obtain a copy of MotorMaster software, the Power Smart High Efficiency Motor Database if you are in Canada, or contact several motor vendors to determine which models offer the best value in terms of efficiency and price. Ask vendors how long delivery would take for the motors you select. Are you satisfied? If not, consider contracting with the vendor to stock those motors, or buy them now to keep as spares. By shopping now you have an opportunity to investigate, compare, and negotiate.

Of course, this approach is not limited to motors. Develop replacement plans for other types of equipment, including transformers, switch gear, drives, pumps and fans that may need to be replaced soon or are critical to your facility's operation.

Predictive and Preventive Maintenance

Motor testing should not be a one-shot project. Use guidelines in Chapter 10 to establish a P/PM program. This means on-going testing to identify potential problems before they cause motor failure and energy losses. The data gathered by your testing should be reviewed regularly to identify trends that may indicate impending problems. Also develop schedules for maintenance and replacement of parts such as drive belts.

Your P/PM program should continually evolve to meet the changing needs of your facility and to incorporate new information you gain. Review equipment failures and accidents for indications of ways to prevent future problems.

Staff Involvement and Training

You and other technical staff are the key to optimizing motor system efficiency. Employees must understand the program's goals and should be motivated to make it successful. Operational staff are often in the best position to identify, develop, and implement energy saving strategies. Staff benefit over the long run from a motor optimization program that results in fewer emergencies, reduced hazards, and an opportunity to learn valuable new skills. Here are some guidelines for successful staff involvement:

- Provide praise, recognition, and other rewards to employees who plan and implement successful energy saving projects. Encouragement motivates employees to make an extra effort to identify and develop energy saving proposals.

- Make sure that operational staff have the information and resources they need to develop energy-saving proposals. One major chemical firm produces its own energy saving manual which contains examples of successful energy management projects. The manual is distributed to all technical staff.

• Encourage cooperation between individuals and divisions. Energy conservation projects often require planning and coordination across divisions. Administrators must encourage cooperation or it won't happen.

• Make sure that employees are allowed to take reasonable risks when trying new technologies. Some energy management projects involve uncertainty. Management must be willing to accept reasonable risk and support technical staff when they deal with unexpected problems.

• Appoint or hire an Energy Manager, a specialist who monitors energy consumption for indications of waste, tracks the energy market for cost saving opportunities, and stays informed about new techniques for improving energy efficiency. Energy Managers often repay their wages many times over in cost savings and other benefits.

Data Files

Would you trust a doctor whose patient records are disorganized? Of course not. Good record keeping is essential for tracking and solving problems. A good filing system lets you track and analyze the data that will be gathered in your P/PM program.

Organize your files so that purchase, technical, and repair documentation for each piece of equipment are kept together. Operation, performance, and test data can be saved as paper files, but a better approach is to record this data in a computer spreadsheet or database. Data in computer format can be easily analyzed and manipulated for trend analysis. If you don't have one already, consider purchasing a portable computer that can be used to input data in the field. This will save steps compared with transferring information from paper records to a central computer. Be sure to observe good computer security by backing up and archiving important files.

Your filing system should be well organized, so current and future staff can easily access information, even when you are not available. Document testing and maintenance schedules, who is responsible for each task, and your replacement plan for each piece of equipment. If a motor failed while you were on vacation would your staff know whether to buy a standard or energy efficient model, and which vendor offers the best value? Can other staff members access motor information if you are out sick or on leave? With a good filing system the right decisions will be made no matter who is in the office.

Investment Analysis Policy

Many of the recommendations in this book require investments to achieve energy savings and increased reliability in your drive system. You need a way to analyze these investments to determine which are cost effective. This process should be as simple as possible while still providing sufficient accuracy. It should be flexible enough to allow non-monetary factors, such as improved reliability and safety, to be given the weight they deserve. Your company may already have such a decision making process. See Chapter 11 for general guidelines.

SUMMARY

Ultimately it is up to you to craft a continuing program that makes use of the information in this book to optimize your electric motor drive system. Your program must include scheduled testing, proper selection of replacement motors and repairs, staff training, record keeping, and economic evaluation. It will involve your superiors, who must support your program, and operation staff who must implement it. The rewards of an effective optimization program include energy savings, increased reliability, reduced hazards and less stress for you and other staff.

Appendix A

Motor Nameplate and Catalog Glossary

This appendix explains the information typically provided on motor nameplates and in motor catalogs.

MODEL NAME

Manufacturers often assign motor model names that indicate special design features. Many manufacturers produce lines of "energy efficient," "high efficient," or "premium efficient" motors. However, in some cases one manufacturer's "standard efficient" motor is actually more efficient than another's "energy efficient" model.

HORSEPOWER OR KW RATING

A motor's rating indicates that model's maximum normal power output. In North America mechanical output power is measured in horsepower. NEMA has established 24 standard motor horsepower ratings from 1/2 to 400 horsepower. In other parts of the world power is measured in kilowatts (kW), and standard kW sizes have been established.

Figure A-1   Motor Nameplate Image

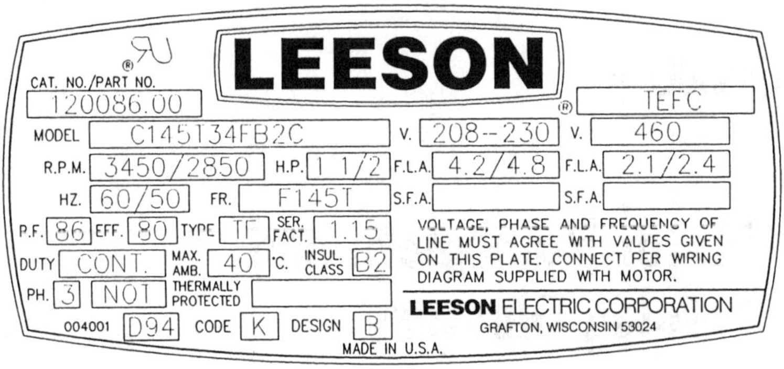

Motor nameplates provide a variety of useful information. Specific nameplate information varies somewhat between different manufacturers and models.

SERVICE FACTOR

This is a multiplier that indicates how much above its full load rating a motor can operate without immediate failure. For example, a 10 horsepower motor with a 1.15 service factor can drive an 11.5 horsepower (8.6 kW) load without burning out. However, operating a motor above its rated load reduces efficiency and reliability.

FRAME SIZE

NEMA has established standard frame dimensions for horizontal motors, to insure that models from different manufacturers are physically interchangeable. Frame sizes are indicated by three digit numbers. The first two digits is the radius of the motor in quarter-inches, the third digit indicates whether it is a long or short frame. A letter at the end indicates the frame series. For example frame size 215T means that the shaft center is 5-1/4" from the mounting surface, and has a longer frame than a 213T. Most motors manufactured since 1964 are T-Frame series, although some U-Frame motors are still produced.

END BRACKET

The part of a motor frame that houses the bearings that support the rotor. Also called the endbell, the endplate, or endshield.

MOUNTING TYPE

There are several standard frame mounting arrangements.

- Horizontal, rigid mounted is most common. Feet are cast or a mounting plate is welded to the body of the frame.

- Vertical shaft frames stand upright. They are often used for pumps.

- C- and D-Face frames are designed to attach by the end face, allowing the motor to be sealed against the equipment it operates. Many manufacturers produce adapters that convert standard horizontal motors to C-Face.

- Resilient mounting uses rubber rings to isolate the motor's vibration from the base.

TORQUE

Torque is a measure of rotational force produced by the motor, measured in pound-feet (pounds of weight on a one-foot lever). There are four different motor torque ratings:

- *Full-Load Torque.* Torque measured at full-load.

- *Locked-Rotor Torque.* The maximum torque that the motor can produce from a complete stop.

- *Breakdown Torque (also called "Pull-Out Torque").* The maximum torque that the operating motor can produce without stalling. It is the highest point on the torque curve.

- *Pull-Up Torque.* This is the minimum torque developed during acceleration between zero and full speed. It is the lowest point on the torque curve.

NEMA DESIGN

Induction motors have been standardized according to their torque characteristics, which are indicated by a NEMA letter codes, Table A-1. Design A and B motors are intended for continuous operation with relatively constant torque. Designs C and D are designed for shorter cycles, fluctuating loads and higher start-up torque requirements. Design D produces maximum torque at startup and has the highest slip. It is often possible to use a smaller motor by selecting a design C or D motor rather than a design A or B for high torque operations. This can reduce your purchase costs, save energy and increase motor reliability.

Table A-1 NEMA Motor Design Characteristics

Design	Starting Torque	Starting Current	Breakdown Torque	Full-Load Slip
A	medium	high	high	low
B	medium	medium	medium	low
C	high	medium	medium	medium
D	highest	low	high	highest

DUTY OR TIME RATING

The duty or time rating is the length of time the motor is designed to operate. Most motors are rated for continuous operation, but others are rated for intermittent duty, such as 5-, 10-, 30- or 60-minute cycles. A motor that is operated at full-load for longer than its duty rating can build up heat, causing winding deterioration and premature failure.

PHASE

Phase indicates whether the motor is built for single- or three-phase operation. Three-phase motors are inherently more efficient and reliable than single-phase.

FREQUENCY

This is the number of electrical cycles per second, measured in Hertz (Hz). Motors are available in either 60 Hz or 50 Hz, the two frequencies normally used in electrical systems. 60 Hz is most common in North America.

SYNCHRONOUS SPEED

This is the speed of the motor's magnetic field, which depends on the motor's wiring configuration (number of poles) and the electrical frequency. Two, four and six pole motors are the most common speeds, and are usually most efficient. Slower motors must be larger to produce a given horsepower, making them more expensive.

ROTATION

The direction in which the motor shaft turns can be either clockwise (CW) or counter clockwise (CCW).

FULL-LOAD RPM OR OPERATING SPEED

The F.L. RPM rating indicates a motor's operating speed when fully-loaded. This is typically 2-4% slower than synchronous speed. For example, a four pole (synchronous speed of 1800 RPM) motor may have a full-load speed rating of 1760 F.L. RPM. This difference between synchronous and loaded speed is called "slip." F.L. RPM numbers stamped on the NEMA Nameplate are rounded to the nearest 5 RPM and might be slightly different from the values published in the manufacturer's catalog.

ENCLOSURE OR HOUSING

There are three common motor enclosure types:

* *Open Drip Proof (ODP)*
  An open enclosure design allows cooling air to circulate between the inside and outside of the motor. Open drip proof motors offer minimal protection against weather and dirt. They are most appropriate for use in a relatively clear and dry environment.

- *Totally Enclosed*
  This enclosure does not allow air to circulate between the inside and outside of the motor frame. To dissipate heat most large size enclosed motors have cooling fins and an outside fan, and are called Totally Enclosed Fan Cooled (TEFC). Smaller enclosed motors often do not need a fan, especially if located in the airstream of a fan they drive. These are called Totally Enclosed Non-Ventilating (TENV).

- *Explosion Proof (EXPL)*
  This is a special type of enclosed motors designed to prevent sparks inside the motor from igniting flammable or explosive materials. The National Electrical Code (NEC) has established categories of motors for various severity of explosion risk. These motors carry an Underwriter's Laboratories (UL) label and may only be repaired by an UL certified shop.

VOLTAGE RATING

This is the voltage at which the motor is designed to operate. Motors are commonly built to operate at 115-, 200-, 230-, 460- and 575-Volts. Many motors are designed to operate at two different voltages, depending on how they are connected. The most common three-phase motor rating is 230/460 Volts. Nameplates often have wiring diagrams indicating how the leads should be connected for each voltage rating. Some motors, called "Tri-Voltage" and labeled 208-230/460, are rated to operate on 208-Volt systems, but are not as efficient or reliable as a motor designed specifically for that voltage.

NOMINAL EFFICIENCY (FULL-, 3/4-, 1/2- AND 1/4-LOAD)

Efficiency is a ratio between output and input energy. Efficiency is usually indicated in catalogs and nameplates as a percentage. Motor efficiency should be measured in the United States using IEEE standard 112, Method B testing protocol. The CSA C390 standard should be used in Canada.

Manufacturers often supply full-, 3/4-, 1/2- and 1/4-load nominal efficiency values in their catalog, based on the results of testing a representative sample of that motor model. NEMA has established a limited list of efficiency values to be used on nameplates. Thus, a motor model's nominal efficiency of 94.8% will be rounded down to a nameplate efficiency of 94.5%.

MINIMUM EFFICIENCY

NEMA has established Minimum efficiencies that are intended to represent the lowest level of efficiency that could be expected for that motor, taking into account typical performance variations among motors of the same design. For example, a motor with a NEMA Nominal nameplate efficiency of 94.5% is assigned a Minimum efficiency of 93.6%. In theory purchasers could demand a replacement if a motor did not perform at least to its minimum efficiency. In practice, purchasers almost never test motors so these values are of little use when evaluating motors.

POWER FACTOR (FULL-, 3/4-, 1/2- AND 1/4-LOAD)

Power factor is a measure of the portion of reactive power produced by the motor. Like efficiency, power factor is usually displayed as a percentage. Low power factor creates losses in the electrical distribution system. Many utilities impose a surcharge on facilities with low power factor. Low power factor can be corrected relatively cheaply using capacitors. Manufacturers often supply power factor ratings at full-, 3/4-, 1/2-, and 1/4-load, although all of these values may not be published in a catalog.

FULL-LOAD AMPERES (FLA)

The FLA rating indicates how much current a motor will draw when operated at nameplate horsepower, frequency and voltage. Motors with two voltage ratings have two FLA ratings.

LOCKED-ROTOR AMPERES (LRA)

This is the current draw when the motor rotor is "locked." Unless a "soft start" control is used, motors will draw their full LRA during startup. This is called "startup" or "inrush" current. Since inrush current is typically several times greater than at full-load, this is the peak amperage that the electrical system must accommodate.

NEMA nameplates have a kVA code letter which indicates the maximum kilovolt-amperes per rated horsepower (kVA/hp) the motor will draw (Table A-2). This code is used when sizing power lines and overload protection. Utilities sometimes specify that motors be no greater then a code "B" starting (3.54 kVA per horsepower).

Table A-2   Selected Nameplate KVA/Horsepower Codes

Letter Code	KVA/HP
A	0-3.15
B	3.15-3.55
C	3.55-4.0
D	4.0-4.5
E	4.5-5.0
F	5.0-5.6
G	5.6-6.3
H	6.3-7.1
J	7.1-8.0
K	8.0-9.0

Excerpt from NEMA Standard
MG1 - 10.37.2

Nameplate codes indicate the starting current the motor will draw. A particular motor's starting current can be estimated from its horsepower rating with the following formula: Locked-Rotor Amps = (1000 x Hp x kVA/HP) / (1.73 x Volts). *If a value falls between two ranges it is rounded down.*

BEARINGS

Nameplates usually specify the types of bearings used in the motor. This is useful information when they are replaced. The drive end bearing is often rated for higher loads than the opposite end. A nameplate may indicate "drive shaft brg: 6309 C3" and "opp dr shaft brg: 6207 C3." The C3 indicates the bearing's internal clearance.

AMBIENT TEMPERATURE

The air temperature surrounding the motor. Often called "room temperature." High ambient temperatures reduces a motor's cooling capacity, increasing its operating temperature.

TEMPERATURE RISE

This indicates the motor's temperature rise in degrees C at rated load, under optimal power quality and ventilation conditions.

INSULATION CLASS

There are three common classes of motor insulation: B, F and H. The higher the letter the more heat rise the insulation can endure without deterioration. Class F and H also don't absorb moisture, which is important if a motor will often sit unused in damp conditions. Insulation class is an important consideration in motor selection since a large percent of motor failures result from winding insulation failure.

THERMAL PROTECTION

A variety of problems, including poor ventilation, overloading, or too many startups in a short period of time can cause a motor to overheat, leading to immediate failure or permanent damage. To prevent this many motors are built with thermal protection which cuts power if the motor gets too hot. The best thermal protection senses temperature in the windings. A motor with nameplate marked "OVER TEMP PROT 1" has overheating protection that will prevent winding temperatures from exceeding that motor's insulation class maximum temperature rise under locked-rotor conditions. If the

motor nameplate is marked "OVER TEMP PROT 2," overload protection will prevent winding temperatures from exceeding that
motor's insulation class maximum temperature rise under continuous
full-load operation.

AMBIENT TEMPERATURE/ALTITUDE

NEMA specifies that normal motors should operate with a maximum ambient air temperature of 140°C (40°F) and a maximum altitude of 3,300 feet (1000 meters). Specially built motors can exceed
these limits.

CATALOG NUMBER

Most manufacturers have a distinctive catalog number for each
motor model to prevent confusion between similar products.

SERIAL DATA CODE

A serial number on the nameplate may provides useful production
information. The first letter is the factory's manufacturing code. The
second letter identifies the month and the last two numbers identify
the production year. For example, C93 represents March, 1993.

LIST PRICE

Manufacturers assign motor list prices which are used as a reference from which actual purchase prices are calculated. Purchasers
typically receive discounts from the list price ranging from 20% to
60% depending on the size of the purchase and the vendor's policies.
Generally a vendor will offer a discount that is consistent for a specific manufacturer, but the discount rate may change with a different
manufacturer or vendor.

Appendix B

Industrial Motor Troubleshooting Chart

Courtesy of Lincoln Electric Company

The following guidelines can help you identify and solve many electric motor problems.

Symptom	Cause	Remedy
Motor does not start.	Blown fuses.	Replace fuses with a rating of at least 125% of nameplate amperes (check against electrical code.) Install "soft start" controls.
	Overload trip.	Check and reset overload in starter
	Improper power supplied.	Compare power supplied to nameplate rating.
	Improper motor connections.	Check connections against diagram supplied with motor.
	Problem with motor starter circuit.	Check for loose wiring and verify that starter is closed.
	Mechanical failure.	Check motor for free rotation. Check bearing lubrication.
	Bad stator coil connection.	Remove end frames and check winding connections.
	Overloaded motor.	Reduce load to see if problem recurs.

Symptom	Cause	Remedy
Motor does not start (continued)	Open motor phase.	Check for non-continuity in lines to motor or in motor itself.
	Defective rotor.	Check for broken bars or end rings. Replace rotor if damaged.
Repeatedly blows fuses.	Shorted stator.	Rewind motor if economical.
Motor stalls.	Inappropriate motor for application.	Review motor selection. Replace with correct size or type if necessary.
	Overloaded motor.	Reduce load to see if that eliminates the problem.
	Voltage too low.	Check electrical system for problems.
	Open Circuit	Check fuses, overloads, pushbuttons, starter, and motor stator.
Motor runs at reduced speed.	Inappropriate motor for application.	Review motor selection. Replace with correct size or type if necessary.
	Voltage too low.	Check electrical system for problems.
	Excessive starting load.	Reduce starting load below motor rating.
	Defective rotor.	Check for broken bars or end rings. Replace rotor if damaged.
	Open motor phase.	Check for non-continuity in lines to motor or in motor itself.
High current.	Short in stator winding.	Rewind or replace motor.
	Bad insulation in leads.	Replace with new.
	Voltage too high.	Correct power supply.
Slow Acceleration	Excessive load.	Reduce starting load.
	Resistive supply circuit.	Check for poor connections and broken strands in wires.
	Defective rotor.	Check for broken bars or end rings. Replace rotor if damaged.
	Voltage too low.	Check electrical system for problems.

Symptom	Cause	Remedy
Wrong direction of rotation.	Wrong phase sequence.	Swap two of three leads at motor or at power supply.
Overheating under load.	Excessive load.	Reduce load below nameplate rating.
	Poor motor cooling.	Clear ventilation and remove dirt.
	Open motor phase.	Check for non-continuity in lines to motor or in motor itself.
	Unbalanced voltage.	Check electrical system for problems.
	Grounded winding.	Check winding for resistance to ground. Repair or replace as needed.
	Shorted winding.	Check winding resistance or pulse response of motor stator. Rewind or replace as needed.
	High resistance power supply.	Check for poor connections and broken strands in wires.
	Rotor rubs stator.	Check for worn bearings or poor end frame machining.
Noisy Operation.	Non-uniform air gap.	Check bearings and brackets for proper fit.
	Excessive belt tension.	Reduce tension to manufacturer's specifications.
	Unbalanced rotor.	Rebalance rotor.
	Defective bearings.	Replace.
Bearings overheated	Bent motor shaft.	Straighten or replace shaft.
	Excessive belt tension.	Reduce tension to manufacturer's specifications.
	Pulleys too far from bearing.	Move pulleys closer to reduce bearing load.
	Pulley diameter too small.	Use larger diameter pulleys.
	Misalignment.	Correct alignment of drive and load.
	Inadequate grease.	Regrease according to manufacturer's specs.

Symptom	Cause	Remedy
Bearings overheated (continued)	Excessive grease.	Reduce grease to level of half of bearing cavity.
	Deteriorated grease.	Regrease according to manufacturer's specs. Remove old grease with hot oil if necessary.
Unequal phase currents.	Unbalanced line voltage.	Check electrical system for problems.
	Open motor phase.	Check for non-continuity in lines to motor and in motor itself.
Scraping sound.	Fan rubbing.	Remove fan cover. Tighten fan mounting as needed.

Appendix C

Motor Purchase Specification Form

Use this form as a model for developing your own motor purchase specifications.

Design Features	
Frame type.	
Frame size.	
Frame mounting arrangement.	
Enclosure type.	
Thermal protection.	
Space heating.	
Ambient temp. over 40°C or altitude over 3,300 ft.	
Special wiring or conduit box location.	
Special features.	
Performance Features	
Horsepower.	
Duty cycle.	
Minimum startup torque.	
Minimum breakdown torque.	
Minimum F.L. Efficiency.	
Minimum 3/4-, 1/2-, or 1/4-load efficiency.	
Minimum power factor.	
Minimum service factor.	
Maximum full-load speed rating.	
Operating voltage and frequency.	
Insulation class and Maximum Temp. Rise.	
Maximum starting current.	
Minimum stall time.	
Inverter application.	

Appendix D

Motor Inventory and Test Form

This form, or a similar version tailored to your procedures, can be reproduced and used when performing motor testing, or a spreadsheet can be developed with these headings for use with a portable computer.

General Information

Staff Name_____   Date:_____

Facility_____   Location _____

Average Energy Rate _____¢/kWh   Average Demand Charge _____ $/kW

Motor Information

Location _____   Supplied By _____

Inventory Code _____   Motor Application_____
                                       Type of equipment the motor drives.

Annual Operating Hours _____   Special Features_____
                                       Vertical shaft, C-Face, integral brake, etc.

Bearing Type *Front* _____   *Back*_____

Visual Inspection Comments _____

Nameplate Data

Make/Model_____   Serial Number _____

Horsepower Rating _____   Frame Size _____

Phase and Hz_____   Voltage Rating _____

Enclosure Type _____   NEMA Torque Class _____

Poles/Synchronous Speed_____   Full-Load RPM _____

Service Factor _____   Insulation Class _____

Temperature Rating_____   FL Amp Rating _____

Other Data _____

Measured Data

Input Volts_____   Input Amps_____
  By voltmeter   *By ammeter*

Input kW _____   Operating Speed_____
  By powermeter if available, otherwise calculate below   *By tachometer*

Measured Temperature _____   Vibration_____
  By internal thermometer if installed   *By vibration analyzer (use standard location)*

Other Test Data _____

Calculated Values

Full Load Slip (FL) Slip _____   Operating Slip_____
  (Synchronous RPM – FL RPM Rating)   *(Synchronous RPM – Operating Speed)*

Load Factor _____   Horsepower output_____
  (As described in Chapter 4)   *(Rated HP x Load Factor)*

kVA input_____   Power Factor _____
  (Input Volts x Input Amps x 0.001732)   *(Average kW/kVA x 100%, or from Figure 5-4)*

Input kW _____   Annual Energy Cost _____
  (By powermeter if available, otherwise   *(Input kW x Annual Operating Hours x Energy Rate)*

Annual Demand Cost (if any)_____   Total Annual Operating Cost_____
  (Monthly Demand Rate x number of months motor   *(Annual Energy + Demand costs)*
  operates during peak demand period)

Maintenance

Belts _____   Mounting Bolts_____
  Indicate adjustment or replacement   *Indicate tightening or other adjustments*

Lubrication _____   Cleaning _____
  Indicate type of lubricant used   *Indicate type of cleaning performed*

Other Maintenance_____

Appendix E

Motor Repair Shop Evaluation

(Courtesy of Steve Darby, Darby Electric)

The evaluation forms in this appendix identify criteria for evaluating motor repair shops. The final page provides a grading system for scoring the results.

Motor Repair Shop Evaluation

Shop Name   Date:

Location   Evaluated By:

Section I Service Capabilities - Pg. 1	Mandatory	Desirable	
AC Random Winding			
Concentric	M		
Lap	M		
AC Form Coil Winding		D	
DC Armature Winding	M		
DC Field & Interpole Winding	M		
Servo Motor Rebuilding		D	
Pump Rebuilding	M		
Variable Speed Transmission Rebuilding	M		
Gear Reducer Rebuilding	M		
Magnet Wire Stock			
15 sizes In Stock	M		
25 sizes In Stock		D	
Rectangular Wire In Stock		D	
Motor Lead Wire			
10 Sizes In Stock	M		

NOTES:

Motor Repair Shop Evaluation

Shop Name   Date:

Location   Evaluated By:

Section I Service Capabilities - Pg. 2	Mandatory	Desirable	
Insulation Used			
Slot Liners	M		
Division Strips	M		
Phase Separators	M		
Wedges	M		
Sleeving	M		
Temperature Controlled Burnout Oven	M		
H_____ W_____ D_____			
Overtemperature Suppression Device	M		
Afterburner To Reduce Atmospheric Emissions		D	
Computer Controlled Coil Winder	M		
Controlled Tension Dereelers	M		
Dip Tank	M		
Diameter_____ Depth_____			
100% Solids Resin			
Polyester_____			
Epoxy_____		D	

NOTES:

Motor Repair Shop Evaluation

Shop Name   Date:

Location   Evaluated By:

Section I Service Capabilities - Pg. 3	Mandatory	Desirable	
VPI System		D	
Diameter_____ Depth_____			
Pressure_____ psi			
Vacuum_____ torrs			
100% Solids Resin		D	
UL Approval To Rebuild Explosion Proof Motors		D	
UL File #_____			
Hardware			
Inch Sizes In Stock	M		
Metric Sizes In Stock	M		
RTD's In Stock		D	
Thermistors In Stock		D	

NOTES:

Motor Repair Shop Evaluation

Shop Name   Date:

Location   Evaluated By:

Section II Mechanical Capabilities - Pg. 1	Mandatory	Desirable	
Lathes To Swing:			
10"	M		
20"	M		
40"		D	
60"		D	
Boring Mill		D	
Size_____			
Horizontal Milling Machine		D	
Power Metal Cutting Saw	M		
Welding			
AC Arc	M		
DC Arc	M		
Metal Inert Gas (MIG) Welding	M		
Tungsten Inert Gas (TIG) Welding	M		

NOTES:

Motor Repair Shop Evaluation

Shop Name   Date:

Location   Evaluated By:

Section II Mechanical Capabilities - Pg. 2	Mandatory	Desirable	
Powder Metal Spray Process	M		
Housing & Journal Electroplating	M		
In-Shop Dynamic Balancing			
25 lb	M		
1000 lb	M		
5000 lb		D	
10,000 lb		D	
20,000 lb		D	
Portable Dynamic Balancing Equipment		D	
Brand_____			
Model Number_____			
Hydraulic Bearing Pullers			
5 ton	M		
20 ton	M		
60 ton	M		
100 ton		D	

NOTES:

Motor Repair Shop Evaluation

Shop Name   Date:

Location   Evaluated By:

Section II Mechanical Capabilities - Pg. 3	Mandatory	Desirable	
Horizontal Press Tons_____ Max Length_____		D	
Vertical Press Tons_____ Max Height	M		
Arbor Press	M		
Induction Bearing Heater	M		
Temperature Indicators To Prevent Overheating Bearings	M		
Commutator Undercutter	M		
Commutator Slotting Saw	M		
Abrasive Grit Blasting Facilities		D	
Glass Bead Blasting Facilities		D	

NOTES:

Motor Repair Shop Evaluation

Shop Name   Date:

Location   Evaluated By:

Section II Mechanical Capabilities - Pg. 4	Mandatory	Desirable	
Recirculating Solvent Cleaner		D	
Steam Cleaner		D	
High Pressure Washer		D	
Parts Washing Machine		D	
Coil End Cutoff Saw		D	

NOTES:

Motor Repair Shop Evaluation

Shop Name   Date:

Location   Evaluated By:

Section III Lifting & Hauling Capabilities - Pg. 1	Mandatory	Desirable	
Cranes			
1 ton	M		
Qty _____ Hook Height			
2 ton	M		
Qty _____ Hook Height			
5 ton	M		
Qty _____ Hook Height			
10 ton	M		
Qty _____ Hook Height			
Wire Slings	M		
Qty _____ Max Length _____			
Nylon Slings	M		
Qty _____ Max Length _____			
Forklifts			
1 ton		D	
2 ton		D	
3 ton		D	

NOTES:

Motor Repair Shop Evaluation

Shop Name   Date:

Location   Evaluated By:

Section III **Lifting & Hauling Capabilities - Pg. 2**	Mandatory	Desirable	
Truck Capacities			
1/2 ton	M		
3/4 ton		D	
2 ton		D	
6 ton		D	

NOTES:

Motor Repair Shop Evaluation

Shop Name   Date:

Location   Evaluated By:

Section IV Technical & Backup Capabilities - Pg. 1	Mandatory	Desirable	
Member of EASA	M		
EASA Technical Manual On Hand	M		
EASA Winding Data On Hand	M		
EASA Warranty Adhered To	M		
EASA Standards Adhered To	M		
Average Years Of Experience Per Shop Employee			
3	M		
5		D	

NOTES:

Motor Repair Shop Evaluation

Shop Name   Date:

Location   Evaluated By:

Section IV Technical & Backup Capabilities - Pg. 2	Mandatory	Desirable	
Library Of Technical Publications To Include:			
NEMA MG 1 Motors & Generators	M		
NEMA RP 1 Renewal Parts For Motors & Generators (Performance, Selection & Maintenance)		D	
AFBMA Std 7 Shaft & Housing Fits For Metric Radial Ball & Roller Bearings	M		
AFBMA Std 20 Metric Ball & Roller Bearings Conforming To Basic Boundary Plans	M		
UL 674 Rebuilding Explosion Proof Motors		D	
ISO 1940/1 Mechanical Vibration - Balance Quality Requirements Of Rigid Rotors Part 1. Determination Of Permissible Residual Unbalance	M		
ISO 2372 Mechanical Vibration Of Machines With Operating Speeds From 10 To 200 rev/sec.	M		
ISO 9000, -1, -2, -3, -4 Quality Management And Quality Assurance		D	
IEEE Std 43 Insulation Resistance Testing	M		
IEEE Std 112 Polyphase Induction Motor Testing	M		
IEEE Std 113 Test Procedure For DC Machines	M		
IEEE Std 432 Insulation Maintenance	M		
IEEE Std 1068 Petroleum & Chemical Industry Motor Repair		D	

NOTES:

Motor Repair Shop Evaluation

Shop Name   Date:

Location   Evaluated By:

Section IV Technical & Backup Capabilities - Pg. 3	Mandatory	Desirable	
Library Of Instruction Manuals On Hand	M		
Written Shop Procedure Manual	M		
Evidence Of In-House Training For Shop Employees	M		
Evidence Of Outside Training For Shop Employees	M		

NOTES:

Motor Repair Shop Evaluation

Shop Name   Date:

Location   Evaluated By:

Section V Test Equipment & Facilities - Pg. 1	Mandatory	Desirable	
Core Loss Tester			
10 KVA	M		
25 KVA		D	
125 KVA		D	
Evidence Of Core Testing Before & After Stripping	M		
Ring Gages Date Last Certified _____			
Thru Bearing Size 312	M		
Thru Bearing Size 318		D	
Bore Gages Date Last Calibrated _____			
Thru Bearing Size 312	M		
Thru Bearing Size 318		D	
Micrometers (.0001)			
1" Date Last Calibrated _____	M		
2" Date Last Calibrated _____	M		
3" Date Last Calibrated _____	M		
4" Date Last Calibrated _____	M		
5" Date Last Calibrated _____	M		
6" Date Last Calibrated _____	M		
7" Date Last Calibrated _____	M		
8" Date Last Calibrated _____	M		
9" Date Last Calibrated _____	M		
10" Date Last Calibrated _____	M		
11" Date Last Calibrated _____	M		
12" Date Last Calibrated _____	M		

NOTES:

Motor Repair Shop Evaluation

Shop Name   Date:

Location   Evaluated By:

Section V Test Equipment & Facilities - Pg. 2	Mandatory	Desirable	
Vernier Calipers			
6" Date Last Calibrated _____	M		
15" Date Last Calibrated _____	M		
40" Date Last Calibrated _____		D	
Vibration Analysis Equipment		D	
Brand _____			
Model Number _____			
Date Last Certified _____			
Surge Comparison Tester	M		
Brand _____			
Model Number _____			
Date Last Certified _____			
HIPOT Tester	M		
Brand of Equipment _____			
Model Number _____			
Date Last Certified _____			
AC Volt Rating _____			
DC Volt Rating _____			

NOTES:

Motor Repair Shop Evaluation

Shop Name   Date:

Location   Evaluated By:

Section V Test Equipment & Facilities - Pg. 3	Mandatory	Desirable	
Motor Test Center			
Ammeter For Each Phase	M		
Volt Meter For Each Phase	M		
AC KVA Rating _____			
230 Volt AC	M		
460 Volt AC	M		
575 Volt AC	M		
2300 Volt AC		D	
4160 Volt AC		D	
Voltage Balance Adjustment For Each Phase		D	
DC KVA Rating _____			
0 - 600 Volts, Infinitely Variable	M		
MG Set On Hand For Generated DC		D	
Motor Bedplate For Vibration Testing		D	
Dynamometers			
5 Hp	M		
25 HP	M		
200 HP		D	

NOTES:

Motor Repair Shop Evaluation

Shop Name   Date:

Location   Evaluated By:

Section V Test Equipment & Facilities - Pg. 4	Mandatory	Desirable	
Megohmeters			
500 Volt	M		
1000 Volt		D	
5000 Volt		D	
Ohmeters			
Bridge Or Digital For Low Resistance	M		
Date Last Calibrated _____			
VOM For Typical Measurements	M		
Date Last Calibrated _____			
Phase Rotation Indicators		D	
Oscilloscope		D	
Growlers			
2"		D	
6"	M		
10"	M		
Dye Penetrant Testing		D	
Ultrasonic Testing		D	
Digital Temperature Probe	M		

NOTES:

Motor Repair Shop Evaluation

Shop Name   Date:

Location   Evaluated By:

Section VI Cleanliness Of Facility - Pg. 1	Mandatory	Desirable	
Disassembly Area(s)			
No Trash Accumulation In Corners	M		
Located Away From Stripping	M		
Located Away From Machine Shop	M		
Tools Neatly Organized	M		
Broom And Trash Bins Present	M		
Copper & Steel Scrap Segregated	M		
Adequate Lighting	M		
Winding Area			
No Trash Accumulation In Corners	M		
Located Away From Stripping	M		
Located Away From Machine Shop	M		
Broom And Trash Bins Present	M		
Adequate Lighting	M		

NOTES:

Motor Repair Shop Evaluation

Shop Name   Date:

Location   Evaluated By:

Section VI Cleanliness Of Facility - Pg. 2	Mandatory	Desirable	
Machine Shop			
Cuttings Swept Regularly	M		
Metal Stock Organized	M		
Cutting Tools Stored Neatly	M		
Precision Gages Stored Carefully	M		
Brooms & Trash Bins Present	M		
Adequate Lighting	M		
Supply Room			
No Trash On Floor	M		
Brooms & Trash Bins Present	M		
Shelves Neat	M		
Bearings Stored Carefully, Unopened	M		
Hardware Organized Neatly	M		
Lubricants Clearly Labeled	M		
Adequate Lighting			

NOTES:

Motor Repair Shop Evaluation

Shop Name   Date:

Location   Evaluated By:

Section VII Record Keeping - Pg. 1	Mandatory	Desirable	
Motor Shop ID Stamped On Each Item To Be Repaired	M		
Job # Stamped On Each Item To Be Repaired	M		
Time Clocks Used For Accurate Billing	M		
Time Recorded By Job Number For Each Employee	M		
Disassembly Check Lists Used	M		
Quality Control Sheets Used For Repair Processes	M		
Assembly Check Lists Used	M		
Winding Data Files Well Organized	M		
All Job Records Kept On File	M		
Formal QC/SPC Program	M		

NOTES:

Motor Repair Shop Evaluation

Shop Name   Date:

Location   Evaluated By:

Section VII Record Keeping - Pg. 2	Mandatory	Desirable	
Varnish Quality Records Kept	M		
Employee Training Records Kept	M		
OSHA Forms Posted And Accident Records Kept	M		
Evidence Of Employee Drug Testing		D	
Material Safety Data Sheets (MSDS) Posted In Shop	M		

NOTES:

Motor Repair Shop Evaluation

Shop Name   Date:

Location   Evaluated By:

Summary Of Scores		Mandatory	Desirable	
Section I	Service Capabilities	Max 21	Max 11	
	Shop Score	_____	_____	
Section II	Mechanical Capabilities	Max 20	Max 17	
	Shop Score	_____	_____	
Section III	Lifting & Hauling Capabilities	Max 6	Max 7	
	Shop Score	_____	_____	
Section IV	Technical & Backup Capabilities	Max 19	Max 6	
	Shop Score	_____	_____	
Section V	Test Equipment & Facilities	Max 34	Max 19	
	Shop Score	_____	_____	
Section VI	Cleanliness Of Facility	Max 25	Max 0	
	Shop Score	_____	_____	
Section VII	Record Keeping	Max 14	Max 1	
	Shop Score	_____	_____	

NOTES:
Any Measuring Device Not Calibrated Or Certified Within The Last 12 Months Should
Not Be Considered For Scoring.

Form MRSE-1   Page 21 of 21

Appendix F

Electric Motor Repair Specifications
(Courtesy of Steve Darby, Darby Electric)

This appendix provides comprehensive motor repair specifications.

Table of Contents

1.0 Introduction 260

    1.1   Scope 260

    1.2   Intent 260

    1.3   Reference Documents 260

    1.4   Approvals...260

    1.5   Definitions 261

2.0 Repair Procedures 261

    2.1   Documentation...261

    2.2   Incoming Inspection...262

    2.3   Dismantling 263

    2.4   Vertical Motors...264

    2.5   Winding Removal 265

    2.6   Core Preparation 266

    2.7   Random Rewinds...267

    2.8   Form Rewinds 269

    2.9   Routine Overhauls 275

    2.10 Rotor Test and Repair 278

    2.11 Shaft Repair...281

    2.12 Anti-friction Bearings 282

    2.13 Babbitt Bearings 283

    2.14 End Brackets 285

    2.15 Other Devices 285

    2.16 Balancing 288

    2.17 Reassembly 289

    2.18 Final Tests 290

3.0 Quality Control 292

    3.1   Measuring Instruments........................292

    3.2   Materials 292

    3.3   Tests and Inspection During Work 293

    3.4   Final Inspection and Test....................294

    3.5   Personnel and Technical Backup...........294

4.0 Documentation 294

    4.1   Purchaser Motor Repair Form..............294

    4.2   Repairer's Quality Record 294

5.0 Repair Shop Evaluation 295

    5.1   Inspection....................................295

1.0 INTRODUCTION

1.1 Scope   This Guideline lists the minimum requirements for the repair and overhaul of polyphase AC squirrel cage induction motors which are sent for repair. All power ranges, voltages and speeds of squirrel cage motors are covered.

1.2 Intent   The intent of this Guideline is to achieve a consistent, high quality diagnosis, repair and/or overhaul to a motor, and to return it to good operating condition with a minimum of delay and cost. Not all portions of the Guideline apply to all work.

Not all repair situations can be covered in this Guideline. In the absence of specific instructions, the requirements shall be to restore the motor to original or better condition.

1.3 Reference Documents   The references to be used in conjunction with this Guideline are the latest editions of the following:

UL   • UL674 Electric Motors and Generators For Use In Hazardous Locations

EASA   • Standards For The Repair of Electrical Apparatus

IEEE   • IEEE Std. 43, Recommended Practice for Testing Insulation Resistance of Rotating Machinery

          • IEEE Std. 522, IEEE Guide for Testing Turn-to-Turn Insulation on Form-Wound Stator Coils for Alternating-Current Rotating Electric Machines – For Trial Use

NEMA   • NEMA Std. MG-1, Motors and Generators

AFBMA • AFBMA Std. 7, Shaft and Housing Fits for Metric Radial Ball and Roller Bearings

1.4 Approvals

hazardous   Motors intended for use in hazardous locations will
locations   have a nameplate to that effect. The repair work shall be done in a facility which has been certified by the Underwriters Laboratories to meet the requirements

of UL674 Qualification of Facilities Engaged in the Repair of Electric Motors and Generators for use in Hazardous Locations. If the explosion-proof characteristics of the motor are not to be maintained, then the nameplate shall be altered to reflect this, and the motor will no longer be considered suitable for use in hazardous areas.

1.5   Definitions

lift   Lift on a vertical motor is the maximum upward shaft movement possible from the rest position of the shaft at room temperature. It is measured by placing the assembled motor in the vertical position on a stand with no additional parts, such as couplings, on the shaft. A dial gauge is used to measure the total movement from the lower position to the upper position in respect to the frame, when the shaft is raised by means that are appropriate to the size of the motor.

Purchaser   Purchaser shall mean the customer requesting services to which this Guideline is applicable.

repairer   Repairer shall mean the person(s) or company(ies) carrying out the work as specified in this Guideline.

2.0   REPAIR PROCEDURES

2.1   Documentation

repair form   **2.1.1**   The motor will be accompanied by a Motor Repair Form which will list the perceived problems, the operating environment, the urgency of the repair, past problems where applicable, the required repair, cost constraints, missing parts and the person to be contacted about the repair. This form shall be used as a guide for the repair. A sample is included in Appendix G.

extra work   **2.1.2**   If tests and inspection indicate that there are problems beyond the initial scope of the listed repair, then the designated person shall be contacted and given a description of the problems, plus an estimate of their effect on delivery and costs.

file   **2.1.3**   The repairer will keep a copy of the Motor Repair Form in the file for the particular job, which shall also contain records of all the work done, problems noted, checks and measurements taken during the work, repairs carried out and the final tests conducted prior to shipping. Requirements for the work, checks and tests are listed in following Sections.

2.2   Incoming Inspection

2.2.1   On receipt of the motor and after reading the repair form, the repairer shall do the initial tests set out below, plus any other tests indicated by the form.

intent   **2.2.2**   The intent of the tests shall be to determine and record the probable cause of failure, if any, and to determine what work is required.

visual   **2.2.3**   A visual inspection shall be made to assess the general condition of the outside of the motor for cracks, broken welds and missing parts.

insulation to ground   **2.2.4**   An insulation resistance test to ground shall be performed, at a voltage suitable for the motor's voltage rating and the apparent condition of the motor. The insulation need not be tested if it is obviously defective. The testing shall be as follows:

- The initial test voltage shall not exceed 1000 volts DC for insulation rated up to 1000 volts and shall not exceed 1.5 times the insulation rating for insulation rated over 1000 volts.

- For motors where there are more than one winding, the insulation shall also be tested between windings, at the test voltage appropriate to the lower voltage winding, with other windings grounded.

- The duration of the insulation test shall be one minute. The temperature and the humidity shall be recorded.

bearings   **2.2.5**   The shaft shall be manually rotated, to check for any obvious problems with the bearings or shaft. If the motor has sleeve bearings, this test may be omitted, but the bearings and journals shall be checked later.

no load run   **2.2.6**   If possible, the motor shall be run on no load, at nameplate voltage and checked for balanced currents and vibration. The readings shall be noted in the job file.

2.3   Dismantling

identify   **2.3.1**   After the incoming inspection, the motor shall
problem   be dismantled to the extent needed to either fully identify or repair the problem, or to do the specified overhaul.

markings   **2.3.2**   End brackets and frames shall be clearly matched-marked.

parts storage **2.3.3** Bolts and small parts shall be stored in dedicated containers and parts from other jobs shall not be kept with them.

insulated **2.3.4** If the motor has insulated bearings, note
bearings which, if any, have the insulation deliberately bridged. The insulation resistance of each insulated bearing shall be at least one megohm with a 500 volt test.

dowels **2.3.5** If dowels or fitted bolts are used to ensure accurate fits, the location of these pieces shall be identified.

explosion **2.3.6** For motors certified for hazardous locations,
proof extra care shall be taken to ensure that joints and flame paths are not damaged during the work. If damage requiring other than normal repair is found, purchaser shall be notified before proceeding with repair.

heavy shaft **2.3.7** For horizontal motors where the shaft/rotor assembly is too heavy to be removed easily by hand, one or two cranes shall be used to move the shaft, with a close fitting pipe installed over one end of the shaft to act as a shaft extension. Attention shall be paid to the following:

- Care shall be taken that the slings do not damage the bearing surfaces or the rotor.

- Under no circumstances shall the stator windings be touched by any of the parts being moved.

2.4 Vertical Motors   Vertical motors shall be dismantled according to the manufacturer's instruction book. The assembly of vertical motors is critical. Particular attention shall be paid to, and records kept of:

- the amount of rotor lift;

- the make and types of bearings, particularly the thrust bearings;

- the arrangement of the thrust and guide bearings, including specially ground mating surfaces;

- the axial and radial clearances (fit) to the shaft and housing;

- the method of lubrication of both upper and lower bearings;

- the method of bearing insulation, if any, and

- any other particular features of the motor configuration.

2.5   Winding Removal

general   **2.5.1**   For motors that are to be rewound, the core shall be stripped, cleaned, tested and repaired.

take data   **2.5.2**   Winding data shall be obtained to permit coil manufacture of either random or formed coils.

core loss   **2.5.3**   A core loss test shall be done on all stators both before and after stripping and iron repair, to check for damaged interlaminar insulation. The tests shall be done at a flux density of (85,000 lines per square inch) rms. Exciting current and watts loss shall be recorded each time, as well as a physical check carried out for hot spots. If data from previous tests are available, the results shall be compared. Testing at other flux densities may be done if original data is available.

hot spots   If any areas are more than 15 C above the average after 10 minutes, or losses are excessive overall either before or after stripping, the situation shall be discussed with the purchaser before proceeding further. For a core without any hot spots, the losses after stripping shall be within 10% of the pre -strip losses. To avoid misleading results, the second core loss test should not be done until the core has been cleaned and dried.

burn out   **2.5.4**   The winding shall be burnt out in a controlled temperature burnout oven where the temperature is limited to 400°C (752°F) by means of fuel control and supplementary (water spray) cooling.

aluminum   **2.5.5**   Frames may be chemical stripped if burnout
frame   facilities are not available. Other methods of stripping may only be used with purchaser approval.

2.6 Core Preparation

clean   **2.6.1**   The stripped core shall be cleaned of all foreign material, such as insulation debris, and dried.

iron repair   **2.6.2**   All obvious iron damage, plus any problems indicated by the core loss tests, shall be repaired, as shall any frame damage.

The method of repair to damaged cores shall be discussed with purchaser and shall be chosen from the following:

grinding   • selective grinding with a small sharp power tool;

machining   • machining with a boring mill or comparable machine, taking care that the laminations are cut cleanly and not burred over. (Care shall be taken, especially on two and four pole motors to maintain a constant air gap. On all motors, the com bined rotor and stator machining shall not increase the total air gap by more than 20%);

spray
between
laminations

• separating laminations and reinsulating with spray on interlaminar insulation;

mica
between
laminations

• inserting split mica between the laminations; and,

restacking

• restacking, with deburred laminations and new interlaminar insulation.

winding
left <u>in</u>

Iron damage repairs where the winding is to be left in the motor are very difficult. A detailed plan shall be proposed to the purchaser before work is commenced, and the purchaser shall be informed of progress.

core loss test **2.6.3**   A final core loss test shall be done as described in sub-section 2.5.3.

2.7   Random Rewinds

winding
details

2.7.1   The total cross sectional area of a turn, the turns per coil, the span and connection of the coils shall not be changed without authorization from engineering and purchaser.

thermal class **2.7.2**   Class F or higher grade materials shall be used throughout. Windings which were originally Class H shall be replaced with a Class H rewind.

sensors

2.7.3   Temperature sensing devices shall be replaced with devices comparable to those previously used.

explosion
proof

2.7.4   If the temperature class of the insulation of an explosion-proof motor has been increased, a temperature sensor shall be installed to monitor and limit the motor surface temperature to the original maximum external temperature. The motor shall be tagged with a warning to the operator that to maintain the hazardous area classification, the sensor must be connected to shut down the motor.

insulation
materials

2.7.5   Insulation shall include, as a minimum, the following components:

turn
insulation

- multiple build coating turn insulation, of polyamide, polymide or a combination of both over polyester, or equivalent;

slot liner

- slot liner extending at least three millimeters past each end of the slot;

separator

- center strip or separator between the top and bottom coil sides in a slot;

wedge

- a top piece to hold the coils in the slot (where needed, a filling piece shall be used to make up any extra space in the slot); and,

phase
barriers

- phase barriers between end turns of different phases. (These shall be trimmed to permit clear air flow.)

end turns

2.7.6   The end turns shall be fully compacted so that there are no loose wires. Both sets of end turns, plus leads and jumpers shall be laced tightly together so that each turn is tied securely to the two adjacent coils.

connections

2.7.7   All connections shall be brazed with materials that will not be subject to corrosion in the specified operating environment. They shall have no sharp edges and shall be insulated with slip on sleeving.

surge test   **2.7.8**   Before impregnation, the winding shall be given a Surge Comparison Test to verify that there are no wrong connections or shorted turns. The peak test voltage shall be two times the nominal line-to-line voltage, plus 1000 volts. Any defects shall be corrected and retested before impregnating. Surge test results shall be recorded in the repairer's job record sheet.

impregnation **2.7.9**   The rewound stator shall be impregnated in one of the following ways:

dip-and-bake •   double dip-and-bake cycle using resin or varnish and a temperature controlled bake oven. (Baking times and temperatures shall be recorded in the repairer's job record sheet.)

trickle   •   a trickle epoxy or polyester treatment where the impregnant is poured into the end turns and slots of a vertical stator which as been heated with controlled electric current to assist in curing the impregnant; and,

VPI   •   a Vacuum Pressure Impregnation (VPI) treatment.

2.8   Form Rewinds

material   **2.8.1**   All materials used shall be rated Class F or higher.

process   **2.8.2**   The post winding VPI method using polyester or epoxy as the impregnant is preferred over other methods of impregnation of the winding as described in sub-section 2.8.17.

coils   **2.8.3**   New coils shall be suitable for use with the impregnation system in use. They shall be insulated with material that will permit the impregnant to fully penetrate all the insulation with the pressures used. They shall all be of consistent shape. Dimensions shall be such as to permit insertion into the slots with a minimum of force.

stranding **2.8.4** Changing the strand dimensions is permitted, when the proper size is not available within the required time, but the total cross sectional area of copper will not be diminished. The new stranding must not permit buckling during the coil forming and handling processes. The modified design shall be approved by engineering.

turn   **2.8.5** The turn insulation shall be such that when
insulation inserted in the core, a single unimpregnated coil shall be able to withstand, from lead-to-lead, a voltage surge ranging from 350 volts times the number of turns in the coil to a maximum value of two times the crest value of the motor's line-to-neutral voltage. This is discussed in more detail in IEEE Std. 522.
Example: For a motor rated at 4000 volts line-to-line with nine turns per coil, the test voltage would not exceed 6500 volts.

ground wall **2.8.6** Ground wall insulation shall be mica based with a protective layer over the insulation to prevent insulation damage during installation.

test voltage The ground wall shall be capable, before impregnation, of withstanding an AC test voltage of the nominal line-to-line motor voltage for one minute. If an AC tester is not available, a 1.67 multiplier shall be applied to the AC test voltage to obtain the equivalent DC test voltage.

anti-corona
paint

2.8.7   Anti-corona paint shall be applied in and beyond the slot portion of coils in motors which originally had anti-corona paint. Unless otherwise approved, the materials and methods shall be as originally supplied.

slot lines

2.8.8   Slot liners shall be used on coils without anti-corona paint if they were previously used on the motor or if there is room in the slot. They shall extend at least three eighths inch beyond the iron at each end. Side and bottom packing shall be used to ensure a snug fit in the slot. With prior approval, slot sized coils may be used without slot liners provided the extra insulation is built into the coils.

insertion

2.8.9   Care shall be taken to ensure the coils are not damaged during insertion, especially in the area near the end of the slots. Excessive distortion of the coils will be avoided by leaving sufficient coils partially removed from the slots as the final coils are inserted and by waxing or heating the coil to make insertion easier.

packing

2.8.10   The top, middle and bottom packing shall be sufficient to ensure a snug fit for the wedge.

wedges

2.8.11   The wedging, if not continuous, shall be placed in similar positions to the original factory wedging. Motors which had magnetic wedges when originally built, shall have magnetic wedges reinstalled to maintain the performance characteristics.

RTDs

2.8.12   Resistance Temperature Detectors (RTDs) shall be installed as follows:

number • Unless otherwise specified, they shall be the same
characteristics number and have the same characteristics as the
original detectors.

stick type • They shall be of the stick type.

dimensions • They shall be at least six millimeters wide and the
length shall be approximately 50% of the slot
length. They shall be inserted in equally spaced
slots, between upper and lower coils, with packing
filling the gap where the detector is not located.

location • The detectors shall be placed in the center of the
slot width and in the expected hottest portion of
the slot length. As far as possible, they shall be in
intimate contact with the upper and lower coils.

• Each detector shall be installed and its leads
brought out so that the detector is effectively protected from contact with the cooling air.

tests **2.8.13** Before connecting, the entire dried winding
shall be subjected to a one minute Hipot test of the
voltage listed in sub-section 2.8.6 and the leakage at
the end of the test shall be noted. RTDs shall be
grounded during this test.

Each coil shall be subjected to a surge voltage at the
level specified in sub-section 2.8.5.
Any coils failing either of these two tests shall be
either replaced or repaired and the test repeated.

bracing **2.8.14** The end turns shall be braced at the points of
the original winding. The acceptable methods of coil
support shall be:

• coil support rings, which shall be either fixed or
floating, as in the original winding, and shall be

as strong as the original rings (Magnetic material shall not be used in the rings. They shall be insulated, or made of insulating material and if necessary, packing shall be put between the ring and the coil before tying the coil to the ring. Regardless of the practice originally followed, each individual coil shall be tied to all support rings.);

- dacron felt spacers between the coils (The spacers shall be of dacron felt, folded over at least once so that they are compressed during insertion. They shall be at least as deep as the coil height. Spacers cut from pre-cured sheet material shall not be used alone.); and,

- an epoxy loaded rope tied inside the knuckle of each coil and overlapping through two knuckles. (The rope shall either be new, or shall have been kept refrigerated before use.)

The twine used for tying shall be compatible with coils and shall not cause abrasion under movement.

connections   **2.8.15**   All connections shall be brazed.

Before insulating, the joints shall be smoothed off to avoid any sharp points which may cause corona or puncture the insulation.

joint
insulation   Joint insulation shall be compatible with the coils and resin, and shall be comprised of the following:

- at least one thickness of flexible tape over the metal (For VPI processes, the tape shall permit resin entry);

- at least one thickness of glass/mica compound tape for every thousand volts of motor rating;

- a layer of protective tape overall; or,

- other method as approved provided they give equal insulation capabilities.

jumpers   Jumpers and leads shall be tied to the coils and to each other wherever they come close or in contact. Dacron felt spacers shall be used where needed, to make the whole structure more rigid.

Leads are discussed in sub-section 2.15.3.

vacuum   **2.8.16**   The resin used with the VPI system shall be
pressure   100% reactive epoxy or polyester, with a viscosity at
impregnation   operating temperature low enough to fully penetrate the tape layers and a gel time fast enough to minimize drainage. It shall be compatible with the coil insulating materials.

resin sample   To ensure quality, a sample of the resin shall have been taken and tested satisfactorily within two months before the motor is impregnated. The results of the resin tests shall be kept on file and a copy of the most recent test kept in the Job Quality Record (see Appendix H).

vacuum/   The vacuum portion of the cycle level shall be at 10
pressure   mm of mercury or less, and the pressure portion of
levels   the cycle shall be at 95 psi or greater. The duration of the cycles shall be sufficient to achieve full impregnation with no voids.

spare coil   A spare coil shall be purchased with each coil order and run through the impregnation process, with one side in a fabricated dummy slot, at the same time as the main winding. A portion of this spare coil shall be shipped with the motor for later use while the other portion shall be used for internal quality control checks. If the spare coil is used to replace one which fails insulation testing, then the coil which is removed from the stator may be used for the impregnation test.

two cycles Each winding will go through at least two vacuum pressure cycles with oven curing after each treatment.

non-VPI **2.8.17** Non-VPI systems may be used with specific approval. The methods of inserting, wedging, testing, connecting and bracing shall be as described in the relevant preceding sections except that for fully pre-cured coils the ground wall AC test voltage shall be twice the nominal line-to-line terminal voltage plus 1000 volts, with a DC conversion multiplier of 1.67.

pressed The coils shall be pressed to shape in the slot section both before and after ground wall application and impregnation.

The coils also shall use the following:

VPI coils • a prewinding vacuum pressure impregnation system;

loaded tape • loaded tape systems which are cured during processing; or,

dip-and-bake • multiple dip-and-bake cycles in Class F varnish.

2.9   Routine Overhauls

testing **2.9.1** After dismantling, the following procedure shall be followed:

• Winding and cooling ducts shall be cleaned, dried and inspected.

insulation
resistance

- Winding insulation resistance shall be tested at 1000 volts DC.

- The duration of the test shall be one minute for random windings and 10 minutes for form windings.

- For form wound windings, the readings shall be recorded every minute, and the polarization index (ratio of 10 minute to one minute resistance) calculated.

- For random wound windings, the minimum acceptable level after one minute, corrected to a 40 C reference temperature by the instrument manufacturer's insulation resistance correction chart, is 100 megohms. Levels less than 100 megohms shall be discussed with the purchaser.

- For form wound windings, the minimum acceptable level after one minute, corrected to a 40 C reference temperature, is 250 megohms. Levels less than this shall be discussed with the purchaser.

- For form wound windings, the polarization index shall be at least two. Levels less than this shall be discussed with the purchaser.

- If satisfactory levels are not attained, the winding shall be recleaned and dried thoroughly at a temperature not exceeding 100°C (212°F), and then retested.

- For form windings, a successful insulation resistance test shall be followed by a withstand test for one minute at a level of two times the line-to-line voltage plus 1000 V DC, or 70% of this level AC.

• After successful insulation resistance to ground
has been achieved, the winding shall be given a
surge comparison test at a level of:

peak voltage =

0.75 x (2 x line-to-line volts + 1000)   (1)

Example: For a 480 volt rated motor, the
peak voltage for a surge test on a used winding would be:

peak voltage = 0.75 x (2 x 480 + 1000)

= 1470 volts (take as 1500)

cleaning   **2.9.2**   The components, including the stator windings, shall be cleaned with hot water and a suitable
detergent after heavy deposits of dirt and grease have
been removed mechanically.

If necessary, brushes shall be used to clean small pas-
sages in components.

Solvents shall not be used to clean insulation, but
may be used on mechanical components of the motor.

drying   All components shall be thoroughly dried at a temperature less than 100°C (212°F), for as long as it takes
to remove all signs of moisture. For windings, this
will be indicated by the insulation resistance reaching
a plateau after some hours of drying.

repairs   **2.9.3**   After satisfactory insulation resistance has
been attained, all loose or damaged wedges, slot
sticks, coil supports etc., shall be replaced or repaired.

dip-and-bake The winding shall then be given a dip-and-bake using
a Class F or higher grade varnish. Immersion and
baking times shall be sufficient to penetrate any
cracks and give a sealed durable finish to the insula-

tion. The repairer shall notify the purchaser if a dip-and-bake is undesirable.

anti-corona
paint
If the winding originally had an anti-corona paint, the manufacturer's recommendations shall be followed for the varnish treatment.

other
2.9.4   The routine overhaul of other parts of the motor shall return the parts to good condition.

reassembly
2.9.5   The assembly of the motor after overhaul is covered in sub-section 2.17.

2.10   Rotor Test and Repair

testing
2.10.1   All rotors shall be given a test for damaged bars, whether the motor is suspect in this area or not.

single-phase
This test shall apply a stable single-phase voltage to the stator of the assembled motor while the shaft is slowly turned through at least one revolution. Any fluctuations of stator current in excess of 5% shall be investigated further.

Other methods may be used if it can be shown that they have a good record of detecting faults.

other rotor
tests
For motors where electrical or mechanical problems with the rotor are suspected, more sophisticated tests shall be used. These include:
- measuring watts and power factor on single-phase tests;
- Growler tests;
- analysis of the amperes, volts and vibration of a loaded motor;
- physical examination;
- ultrasonic examination of the bars and end rings; and,
- core loss tests.

fabricated   **2.10.2**   Since repair of squirrel cages can be expen-
cage repair   ive, no work shall be done in this area without
approval.

swaging   **2.10.3**   If inspection reveals that the bars are merely
loose in the cage and there are no cracked or broken
bars or joints, the bars shall be fixed firmly in the
slots by swaging each bar at a minimum of three
points along the slot. The bar shall be deformed so
that it fits snugly in the slot by indentation of the top
surface of the bar.

It is understood that with some forms of rotor construction, this method may not be practical, and in
these cases other methods may be proposed.

joint repair   **2.10.4**   If it is only necessary to repair some joints,
the end ring shall be removed, all mating surfaces
shall be cleaned and the joints remade as described in
sub-section 2.10.6. Care shall be taken not to damage
any other components during the dismantling.

The length of bar extending from the rotor core shall
not be changed without specific approval.

cage   **2.10.5**   For cage replacement, the conductive, metal-
replacement   urgical and strength characteristics of both the bar
and end ring materials shall be determined and equivalent materials used.

Since changing the rotor resistance has major effects
on the motor performance, no change in resistance is
permitted.

The cage shall be removed without damage to the
core.

Any parts that are to be reused will be cleaned and examined for defects.

The new bars shall be machined to be a snug fit in the slot (i.e., some force is required to push them into the slot).

brazing   **2.10.6**   The bars shall be brazed or welded to the end rings with material that is not subject to chemical attack by the contaminants listed by the purchaser on the Motor Repair Form for the particular motor.

Brazing shall be done as rapidly as possible in one continuous operation.

testing   **2.10.7**   After fabrication, the joints shall be examined and tested by ultrasonic or comparable means, and the bars swaged in place.

balance   **2.10.8**   The rotor shall be balanced to the tolerances listed in sub-section 2.16 of this Guideline.

cast rotor   **2.10.9**   A defective cast cage shall not be repaired
repair   without prior authorization from the purchaser.

The method of repair shall be to remove the old cage by chemical means, without damaging the laminations, followed by rebarring with extruded aluminum bars and duplicate cast aluminum end-rings using the methods described in sub-section 2.10.5 to 2.10.8 to give the same cage resistance as before.

iron repairs **2.10.10**   If tests or observation indicate that the laminations have been damaged, they shall be repaired or replaced with new laminations. Care shall be taken to ensure a consistent air gap. The total of both stator and rotor machining shall not increase the air gap by more than 20%.

balance   This shall be followed by balancing to the tolerances specified in sub-section 2.16.

Because of the costs involved, this work shall not be done without approval.

2.11   Shaft Repair

general   **2.11.1**   If information on the Motor Repair form, or any tests indicate that there may be a shaft problem, it shall be tested and repaired or replaced. Depending on the damage and the repair shop's capabilities, the method of repair may include welding, metal spraying, plating, grinding, straightening, or in exceptional cases, adding a "stub" shaft.

requirements   **2.11.2**   When the work is completed, the shaft shall meet the following criteria:

total   • It shall be straight, with a Total Indicated Runout
indicated   (TIR) when measured in V blocks, of no more
runout   than 0.05 mm (.002 in) for shafts up to 41 mm (1 5/8") diameter, and 0.08 (.003 in) for larger shafts.

no cracks   • It shall have no cracks. Ultrasonic, magnetic particle, dye penetrant or other testing methods may be needed to verify this.

straight   • It shall be straight, parallel and undamaged at the bearing areas.

journal   • Journal repairs by welding or plating, followed by
repairs   machining and grinding shall return the shaft to the size specified, by the anti-friction bearing manufacturer for the application, or to give the correct clearance, as listed in sub-section 2.13 for a babbitt bearing.

journal   • The TIR in the journal area of a sleeve bearing
runout   motor shall not exceed 0.013 mm (.0005 in) when
                   measured with the shaft supported in narrow V
                   blocks.

fit to rotor • It shall be a tight fit to the rotor iron. If there is
                   looseness, the shaft shall be replaced, except
                   when purchaser and the repairer believe that
                   welding will give satisfactory results.

shaft material • New shafts shall be machined from AISI Gr.
                   C1045 hot rolled steel or equivalent. For special
                   applications, the repair shop and the manufacturer
                   will consult.

tolerances   • In general, shaft dimension tolerances shall be
                   within the limits specified in NEMA MG-1,
                   Motors and Generators, Sections 4.05 to 4.09.

proximity   • For motors with proximity probes, the area under
probes   the probes shall have mechanical runout less than
                   0.013 mm (.0005 in) and total electrical and
                   mechanical runout less than 0.018 mm (.0007 in).
                   Grinding and demagnetizing may be needed to
                   achieve this.

2.12 Anti-Friction Bearings

new bearings **2.12.1**   Anti-friction bearings shall be replaced with
                the same type as originally used, unless otherwise
                approved by the purchaser. If the bearing type, size,
                sealing, shielding or configuration is changed, this
                shall be noted on the nameplate. Purchaser reserves
                the right to specify the bearing manufacturer.

shielding   **2.12.2**   If the method of shielding, sealing or lubri-
sealing   ating is to be changed, it shall be approved by the
                purchaser.

clearance	**2.12.3** Unless otherwise specified, C3 clearance bearings shall be used for all bearings.
tolerances	**2.12.4** Fitting tolerances to the journals and housings shall be to the recommendations for electric motors found in AFBMA Std. 7.
heating	**2.12.5** The bearing shall be heated up, without use of direct flame, to a temperature sufficient to permit it to be slid easily onto the shaft up to the shoulder.
grease	**2.12.6** Greasable bearings shall be lubricated with the recommended grade and quantity of grease.
oil mist	**2.12.7** On motors which use oil mist bearing lubrication systems, care shall be taken to ensure the shaft seals are in good condition, and there are no blocked passages.

2.13   Babbitt Bearings

checks	**2.13.1** Babbitt bearings shall be checked for wear, clearances to the journal and housing, and obvious damage.
wear patterns	Abnormal wear patterns shall be noted and discussed with purchaser.
clearances	Clearances to the journal should be within the original manufacturers specifications if known, otherwise see the EASA standard 2.2.2. Clearances outside this range shall be discussed with purchases.
babbitt adhesion	There should be no visible separation of the babbitt from the backing material.
repair	**2.13.2** Minor problems shall be fixed by machining, scraping and polishing, followed by rechecking.

Other problems shall be remedied by replacement or rebabbitting the bearing, the choice being made on economic and technical grounds after consultation between purchaser and the repairer.

rebabbitting   **2.13.3**   When rebabbitting bearings, the following shall be observed:

centrifugal   • Centrifugal casting shall be used with thorough
casting   cleaning and preparation of the backing metal.

lead free   • The babbitt shall have high tin content and shall be lead free.

bond   • After initial machining, the bond of babbitt to backing metal shall be verified ultrasonically to be more than 80%.

machine   • The bearing shall be machined to the specified clearance, and oil grooves, RTD pockets and other features that were in the original bearing, duplicated.

check fit   • The bearing shall be checked for fit to the shaft by blueing and checking the contact pattern after assembly, rotation and dismantling of the bearing. The bearing shall be scraped and polished until a uniform contact pattern is achieved.

clearance   • Clearance shall be checked with a plastigage or equivalent method, to be within the specified range.

insulated   **2.13.4**   Insulated bearings shall have an insulation
bearings   resistance of one mogohm when measured with a 500 volt device.

oil rings   **2.13.5**   Oil rings shall be round within 0.025 mm (.001 in) and shall have no rough edges. Replacement rings shall be machined from the same material as the original rings.

2.14   End Brackets

requirements   **2.14.1**   End brackets shall be snug fits to the stator frame.

Dowel holes and rabbit fits shall not be worn.

clearances   **2.14.2**   Clearances to the outer sections of anti-friction bearings shall be within the tolerances specified by AFBMA Standard 7.

repairs   **2.14.3**   Repairs to end brackets shall be by building up the metal and machining to size. Welding, plating and sleeving are the accepted methods.

Epoxies and other compounds shall not be used for locking bearings.

2.15   Other Devices

fans   **2.15.1**   Fans shall be checked for cracks and fit to the shaft or rotor.

fixing fans   They shall be firmly fixed to the shaft or rotor by the original factory method, unless there has been corrosion between dissimilar metals, in which case a new method shall be proposed. Welding to the shaft is not permitted.

Repairs to fans shall only be done after discussion with purchaser.

new fans   New fans shall be as supplied by the original manufacturer unless the design appears to be defective, in which case purchaser and the repairer will discuss a new arrangement.

hazardous   Fans used in motors for use in hazardous locations shall be made of material which will not cause sparking, either by impact or by build up of static electricity.

temperature sensors   **2.15.2**   Temperature sensors will be installed in the motor as required.

winding RTDs   Winding RTDs are discussed in sub-section 2.8.12.

bearing RTDs   Bearing RTDs shall be of the same type as those removed and shall be located to sense, as nearly as possible, the highest babbitt temperature. If the original bearing RTD was insulated, the replacement shall also be insulated.

thermistors   Thermistors, thermocouples and other devices shall be as per the original and will usually be located in the end turns.

leads   **2.15.3**   Leads shall be flexible and multi-stranded, and have the same cross sectional area and temperature class as the original leads.

marking   Main power and accessory leads shall be indelibly marked using the same marking systems as the incoming motor. If this is illegible then the system described in NEMA MG-1, Motors and Generators, Section 2 shall be used and a notice describing the system attached to the terminal box. Every effort shall be made to keep the original direction of rotation.

lugs   Lugs, if used, shall be suited for the application and have all cable strands in the lug. No cable strands may be cut off or bent back to facilitate insertion in the lug.

If crimp lugs are used, the correct make and style of die shall be used for the particular lug, and the correct compression applied.

junction boxes

2.15.4 Junction boxes shall be returned to original condition. In particular, the following items must be confirmed.

- Missing bolts for both the cover and the motor-to-box joint shall be replaced.

- On motors certified for hazardous environments, the junction boxes shall be sealed off from the main body of the motor by a sealing compound.

- Damaged flanges shall be repaired. No paint or gaskets shall be left on the flanges of boxes for explosion-proof motors.

space heaters **2.15.5**   Space heaters shall be tested for insulation resistance for one minute at 500 volts. A 10 megohm resistance is acceptable.

They shall be tested for correct functioning with their rated supply voltage.

Since purchaser does not always use the heaters, check with purchaser before replacing heaters.

vibration sensors

2.15.6 Vibration sensors shall be replaced in their original locations.

Where proximitors are used, care shall be taken that they are adjusted so they do not touch the shaft.

Detailed set up of proximitors will be done by purchaser on site.

surge equipment

2.15.7 Surge capacitors and arresters shall be tested by:

- testing the capacitors' insulation resistance at 1000 volts (normally the discharge resistor will give a reading of less than 30 megohm);

- applying a DC Hipot test to the arrester at 80% of its rating. (It should not break down at this level.) For a 4.5 kV arrester, the test voltage would be

  voltage = 4.5 x 1.4 x 0.8 = 5kV); and,

- alternately, using a surge tester on the windings with the surge equipment both connected and disconnected. (There should be a much less steep wavefront with the equipment connected.)

Leaking capacitors, or components which fail the tests shall be replaced.

2.16 Balancing

motors

The motor rotor shall be balanced in a balance stand before assembly of the motor. Balance criteria include the following:

half key

- It shall be balanced with a half key in the keyway or with sheave or a half coupling and full key.

tolerance G2.5

- Generally, the permitted total unbalance is $15w/n/2 = $ oz in/plane where W is weight of rotor in pounds and N is operating speed in RPM. The total unbalance shall be split roughly equally between the two planes.

tolerance G1.0

- Two Pole rotors should be balanced to $6W/n/2 = $ oz.in./plane.

material removal

- If material is removed, structural integrity and fan efficiency shall be maintained.

added   • Added material shall be able to withstand the cen-
material   trifugal forces and be positioned either in the man-
               ufacturer's designated positions and locked in
               place, or positioned in a location where centrifu-
               gal force will tend to keep the material in place.
               Weights may be attached to metallic parts only.

2.17   Reassembly

requirements The assembly of the motor is the reverse of the disas-
               sembly process and the following points shall be
               observed:

               • Match marks shall line up.

               • On reinsertion of the rotor, take care not to dam-
                 age the journals or the stator windings. Cranes,
                 slings and extension pipes shall be used on heavy
                 rotors.

               • Dowels and fitted blots shall go back into the
                 same holes as they came from.

               • Where they can be measured, all air gaps shall be
                 within 10% of the average.

               • On motors with insulated bearings, the insulation
                 shall be checked and noted.

               • On vertical motors, the lift on the shaft shall be
                 the same as the original manufacturer's setting,
                 unless purchaser and the repairer agree that a
                 modified setting would give better performance.

               • Motors for use in hazardous environments shall
                 have all the explosion-proof features maintained
                 and verified.

2.18   Final Tests

insulation   **2.18.1**   Prior to running, the motor shall be given an insulation resistance test to ground in the following manner:

random   • For random wound motors, a test at 1000 volts
wound   DC for one minute shall be done. Readings corrected to 40 C, which are less than 100 megohms, shall be discussed with purchaser.

form wound • For form wound motors, a polarization index test at 1000 volts DC for 10 minutes shall be done. Corrected readings less than 500 megohms, or polarization indexes less than two, shall be discussed with purchaser.

withstand   • For form wound motors, a DC withstand test at two times the nominal voltage, plus 1000 volts, shall be carried out for one minute. Thus, for a 4000 volt motor, the withstand test shall be 9000 volts for one minute. Alternatively, an AC test voltage of 70% of the DC level may be used.

running test **2.18.2**   After the insulation tests, the motor shall be run on no load at full terminal voltage, with either a half key or a half coupling, on the shaft. If the motor uses an external oil supply and removal system in normal use, a similar system shall be arranged for the test. The test shall determine that:

no load amps • No load currents at rated voltage shall be essentially balanced for balanced supply volts.

vibration,   • On motors rated less than 100 HP vibration shall
small motors   be in conformance with EASA Standard 6.4.6.3 Quality Grade A.

vibration,   • On motors rated 100 HP and over, hard copy hor-
large motors   zontal, vertical and axial readings shall be taken
at each bearing and shipped with the report.
Tolerance shall not exceed EASA Standard
6.4.6.3 Quality Grade A.

temperature   • Temperature rise after 15 minutes running on
rise   motors rated less than 200 HP and one hour or
until levels stabilize on larger motors, shall be
within normal limits on the frame and bearings.
On the larger motors, all final RTD readings shall
be recorded.

insulated   • On motors with insulated bearings, the voltage of
bearings   the uninsulated bearing shall be checked. If the
voltage is more than 0.1 volts, AC or DC, the
bearing insulation shall be rechecked.

magnetic   • On motors with sleeve bearings, the magnetic
center   center location shall be verified and oil ring rotation confirmed.

shipment   • At the completion of the test, the motor shall be
drained of any oil used for the test, painted and
prepared for shipment. Any drained oil sumps
shall be marked with a tag advising to refill the
sump before operation. Oil and coolant inlets and
outlets shall be plugged and masked before painting and shipping.

block shaft   • Motors shall have their shafts blocked to prevent
axial and radial movement during shipping.

3.0 QUALITY CONTROL

3.1 Measuring Instruments

calibration   **3.1.1**   All measuring instruments shall be calibrated regularly. The calibration records shall be available for purchaser inspection. Minimum frequency of calibration shall be annually, except:

insulation testers
- insulation resistance testers – every three months to a known resistance. (Battery powered units shall be checked for battery condition before and after each set of readings.);

dimension meters
- micrometers, vernier calipers and other dimension measuring devices – every three months; and,

bore gages
- bore gages shall be calibrated to a certified standard before and after each use.

storage   **3.1.2**   All measuring equipment shall be stored in a clean dry place.

3.2 Materials

anti-friction bearings   **3.2.1**   Anti-friction bearings shall be the same type as originally used, unless otherwise specified by purchaser. In general, only metallic cages shall be used.

They shall be stored in their factory packaging in a clean, dry, vibration free location.

solid insulation   **3.2.2**   Insulating materials such as slot liners, tapes and phase insulation shall be rated for the temperature class of the motor and shall be compatible with the resins used.

Specifications for the materials shall be obtained from the material supplier and kept for checking their suitability for the application.

The materials shall be stored in a clean, dry location. Material such as B stage tape that degrades with time at room temperature, shall be kept refrigerated.

resins and
varnishes

3.2.3 The manufacturer's material specifications for resins and varnishes shall be kept on file, to permit checking for correct storage, handling and usage.

A sample shall have been taken and analyzed to the satisfactory within two months of its being used on a motor.

other
materials

3.2.4 Other materials shall be new and of good quality. In particular the following shall be confirmed:

lead wires

- Lead wires shall be multi-stranded and flexible with insulation rated for the temperature and voltage class of the motor.

magnet wire

- Magnet wire for random-wound motors shall be compatible with the other insulation system components and shall be insulated with a polyamide, polyimide or a combination of both, over a polyester base coat, or equivalent. Any wire damaged in storage or working shall be replaced. The manufacturer's specifications for the insulation shall be kept on file for reference.

formed coils

- All the formed coil supplier's quality assurance data shall be supplied with the coils and shall be included with the quality record for the motor.

3.3   Tests and Inspection During Work

records

3.3.1 Records shall be kept of all tests and inspections carried out during the work. Signed copies of these records shall be shipped in original form, at the same time as the motor, to the designated contact person.

access   **3.3.2** Purchaser shall have access to the repair facilities at all times that work is being done, for the purposes of checking progress and inspecting the work.

3.4   Final Inspection and Test

Purchaser   For all motors over 200 HP, and other critical motors,
to be   purchaser shall be informed when the final inspection
informed   and testing of the motor is to take place. Purchaser shall have the right to be present for tests on any motors.

In emergency cases, tests will not be held up waiting for purchaser people, but every effort shall be made to keep purchaser informed so that they can be present if possible.

All final inspection and test results shall be sent, in their original form, to the designated contact person.

3.5   Personnel and Technical Backup

employees   **3.5.1** Employees shall be trained and experienced to the level required for the work being done.

backup   **3.5.2** The repairer shall either belong to the Electrical Apparatus Service Association, or shall have an engineering department with people trained and experienced in motor design and application.

4.0 DOCUMENTATION

4.1   Purchaser Motor Repair Form   A Motor Repair Form is attached in Appendix G. One of these forms will normally accompany each motor sent out for repair.

4.2   Repairer's Quality Record   A sample Repairer's Quality Record Form is attached in Appendix H. Either this form, or the repairer's approved equivalent form shall be used on each motor.

5.0 REPAIR SHOP EVALUATION

5.1 Inspection

general   **5.1.1** All repair shops doing business with purchaser will be inspected and evaluated. The results of the evaluation will determine what type and rating of motor will be sent to particular shops.

The results of the evaluation will be discussed with each shop, if desired.

factors   **5.1.2** The factors in the evaluation will be:

- capacity and condition of lifting equipment;

- winding and insulation equipment and tools;

- mechanical capabilities;

- technical capabilities and backup;

- quantity and quality of test equipment;

- shop cleanliness;

- record keeping; and,

- the proportion and type of work sent to sub-contractors, and the abilities of the sub-contractors to meet the above factors.

Appendix G

Electric Motor Repair Form
(Courtesy of Steve Darby, Darby Electric)

This form can be used to record standard information on motors being delivered for repair.

MOTOR REPAIR FORM

Repairer:		Date:
Motor Designation:		Site:
Manufacturer:	Type:	Power:
Volts: Amperes:	Speed:	Frame:
Serial No.:	Bearings:	Lubricant Grade:
Other:		

Service: Contamination H$_x$S (   )

Other (specify)
_____

Reason sent for repair:

_____

Required work:

_____

Past problems with machine:

_____

Missing parts:

_____

Urgency: (check one)   Cost limitations:

Rush, Full O.T.   (   )   Contact with price before work   (   )

Rush, Limited O.T.   (   )   Go ahead, advise price   (   )

A.S.A.P., No O.T.   (   )   Other _____   (   )

Routlne (specify time)   (   )

Hold Points if required   (   )
_____

Special instructions:

contact: Phone:
reference:

Appendix H

Electric Motor Repairer's Quality Record

(Courtesy of Steve Darby, Darby Electric)

These forms can be used by repair shops to record standard information on motors as they are received and repaired. Copies of the completed forms should be maintained by the motor owner and repair shop for future reference.

REPAIRER'S QUALITY RECORD – INDUCTION MOTOR
(Attach other notes and test results as needed (page 1 of 3)

Shop Job:	Reference:		Date In:
Location:		Contact:	
Work Requested:			
Nameplate Data:			
Manufacturer:	Power:	Speed:	Frame:
Serial No.:	Volts:	Amps:	Type:
Bearings: DE	NDE	Insulation Class	
Other:			
Extra/Missing Parts:			

INCOMING TEST VISUAL:

I.R.: _____ MΩ at _____ V, _____ C, _____ % R.H.

Leads marking: _____ Size _____

Other electrical: _____

Coupling Fit: _____ OK/not OK, Other _____

No load at: _____ V, Amperes: A _____, B _____, C _____

Vibration: DE: _____ H, _____ V, NDE: _____ H, _____V

Rotor bar test at: _____V, _____ A, _____ OK/not OK _____

Other: _____

REPAIRER'S QUALITY RECORD – INDUCTION MOTOR
(Attach other notes and test results as needed (page 2 of 3)

Shop Job:	Reference:	Date In:
Location:	Contact:	

DISMANTLED VISUAL:

Surge test at: _____ V, OK/not OK

Core loss tests at: _____ lines/cm2, Before strip _____ W/kg,_____ Hot spots Y/N
(attach detailed results)   After Strip _____ W/kg, _____ Hot spots Y/N

Bearing fits: D.E.   N.D.E.
   Journal   _____   _____
   Housing: _____   _____

Other:

_____

WINDING DETAILS: (for form wound stator use Fig. B.1)
Slots _____   Span_____   Connection _____
Coil turns_____   parallels _____
Bracing _____   Conductor size _____
Insulation details:

_____

REWINDS:
Surge test at: _____ V, OK/not OK
Hipot/Megger at _____ V, _____ minutes, _____ leakage/I.R.
Coil bracing:_____
Resin last tested: _____ Bake temp: _____ C, _____ hours
VPI: Vacuum _____ mm, Pressure_____ kPa
       Cycle Time _____ hours Cycle Time _____ hours

REPAIRER'S QUALITY RECORD – INDUCTION MOTOR
(Attach other notes and test results as needed (page 3 of 3)

Shop Job:	Reference:	Date In:
Location:	Contact:	

ROTOR REPAIR DETAILS:

SHAFT REPAIR WORK:

	D.E.	N.D.E.	Specified Figure	
TIR at coupling	_____	_____	_____	Fan _____
Journal diameter	_____	_____	_____	
A/F bearing type	_____	_____	_____	Coupling/Keyway_____
Fit to shaft	_____	_____	_____	
Fit to housing	_____	_____	_____	Balance to _____
Sleeve bearing -				
Journal clearance	_____	_____	_____	
Housing clearance	_____	_____	_____	

OTHER WORK:

FINAL TESTS:

I.R.: _____ MΩ at _____ V, _____ C, _____ % R.H.

Polarization index = _____, Withstand at _____ V, _____OK/not OK

N.L. run at:_____ V, Amperes: A _____, B _____, C _____

Vibration F.O.:   D.E. _____H, _____, V, _____ A
(over 150 kW attach
Spectra to 500 Hz) N.D.E. _____H, _____, V, _____ A

OTHER TESTS:

Tested by:	
Date shipped:	Carrier:
Additional notes:	

ELECTRIC MOTOR REPAIR

Date: _____

CUSTOMER | APPLICATION

NAME PLATE DATA

MAKE

TYPE – SYNCHRONOUS – WOUND ROTOR – INDUCTION

HP-KW	VOLTS	PHASE	SEC VOLTS	POWER FACTOR
RPM	AMPERES	CYCLE	SEC AMPERES	SO NO.
TYPE	FRAME	TEMP. RISE	MODEL	SERIAL

WINDING DATA

INSULATION CLASS   F - H

CONNECTION	NO. OF SLOTS	WIRE SIZE	COIL WEIGHT	WEDGES PER SLOT
CONNECTED 1 – 4 or 1 – 7	COILS IN SLOTS 1 –	SKETCH WIRES IN PARALLEL	DETECTORS	WEDGE LENGTH
GROUPING	TURNS PER COIL	WIRE TYPE	WEDGE SHAPE	WEDGE TK

Coils made right hand ☐ A right hand coil has the top side to the right, looking at connection end.

Coils made left hand ☐ A left hand coil has the top side to the left.

STATOR AND WINDING DIMENSIONS

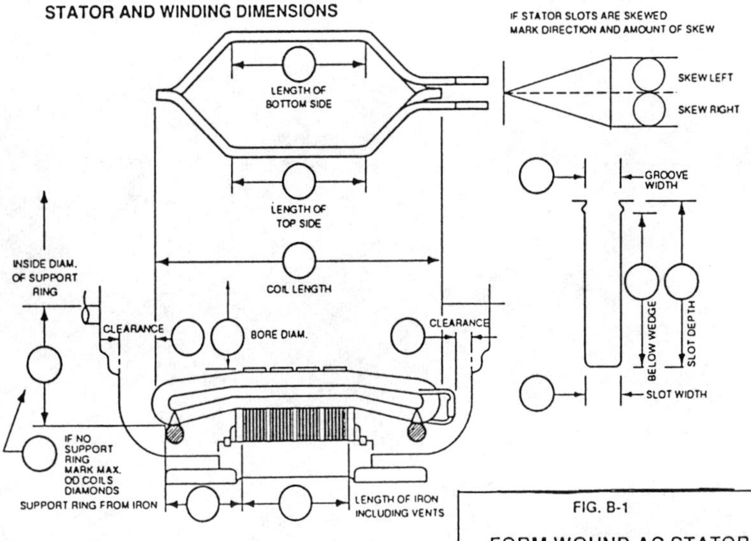

IF STATOR SLOTS ARE SKEWED
MARK DIRECTION AND AMOUNT OF SKEW

FIG. B-1

FORM WOUND AC STATOR DIMENSIONS & WINDING DATA

DWG# EC 90-145	DATE 90-05-03	REV.#

Appendix I

Resources

I-i. ORGANIZATIONS

Electric Ideas Clearinghouse and Bulletin Board Service
P.O. Box 43171
Olympia, WA 98504-3171

	Pacific Northwest	Other Western States	Other Regions
Voice	(800) 872-3568	(206) 956-2237	(206) 956-2237
Modem	(800) 762-3319	(800) 797-7584	(206) 586-6854
Fax	(800) 872-3882	(206) 586-8303	(206) 586-8303

The Electric Ideas Clearinghouse provides free information for energy conservation professionals, including technical, product and policy issues. The Clearinghouse computer bulletin board allows energy professionals to share information and access files, software, a training calendar, and job listings.

Electrical Apparatus Service Association, Inc. (EASA)
1331 Baur Blvd., St Louis, MO 63132
(314) 993-2220; Fax (314) 993-1269

EASA is the major trade organization for electric motor repair shops, with more than 2,600 members, representing about half of all such businesses. EASA provides technical data, training and support to its members.

Institute of Electrical and Electronics Engineers (IEEE)
445 Hoes Lane, P.O. Box 1331
Piscataway, NJ 08855-1331
Phone: (800) 678-IEEE; (908) 981-1393
Fax: (908) 981-9667

Professional organization of engineers which establishes many of the standards used in motor design, testing and operation.

Motor Challenge Program
P.O. Box 43171
Olympia, WA 98504-3171
Phone: (800) 862-2086
Fax: (206) 586-8303

The Motor Challenge is a U.S. Department of Energy program to encourage and support use of energy efficient electric motor systems. This is a joint effort between government, industrial motor users, motor manufacturers and distributors, designers and specifiers, and other key players. The program distributes MotorMaster software and other information on energy efficient motor systems, and provides technical advice to help users join the Motor Challenge and select the best motor for specific applications. Use of the Clearinghouse is free.

National Electrical Manufacturers Association (NEMA)
2101   L Street, NW, #300
Washington DC, 20037
Phone: (202) 457-8400
Fax: (202) 457-8411

NEMA is a nonprofit trade organization of companies that manufacturer electrical generation, transmission, distribution, control and end-use equipment. It establishes and publishes many of commonly used standards that apply to motors and motor controls.

National Fire Protection Association (NFPA)
Batterymarch Park
Quincy, MA 02269
Phone: (800) 344-3555; (617) 770-3000
Fax: (617) 984-7057

The NFPA is a nonprofit organization that establishes fire safety codes and standards. Useful publications include the National Electrical Code and Standard 70B, which covers electrical equipment maintenance.

Underwriters Laboratories
P.O. box 75330
Chicago, IL 60675
Phone: (708) 272-8800

Insurance safety organization establishes standards for many electrical products, including explosion proof electric motors.

I-ii DOCUMENTS

John Andreas, *Energy-Efficient Electric Motors: Selection and Application;* Marcel Dekker, New York, 1992.

M.H. Box and M.V.Brown, "What's in a Nameplate?", *Power,* July 1991, pp. 51-53.

Martin Clifford, *Modern Electric/Electronic Motors;* Prentice Hall, Englewood Cliffs.

Michael Cohen, "Predictive Maintenance of Operational Motors Using Digital Data Collection and Trend Analysis", *Tappi Journal;* January 1991, pp. 151-155.

Murray Dalrymple, "PM Programs Reduce Motor Failures", *EC&M;* October 1984, pp. 34, 174-175.

E. Steve Darby, "Electric Motor Rewinding Should Maintain or Enhance Efficiency", *IEEE Transactions on Industrial Applications;* Vol. 1A-22, No. 1, Jan/Feb. 1986, pp. 126-132.

Electrical Apparatus Service Association, *Guidelines for Maintaining Motor Efficiency During Rebuilding; Electrical Engineering Pocket Handbook,* EASA, 1331 Baur Blvd., St. Louis, MO 63132, (314) 993-2220.

Electrical Apparatus Service Association, *How To Get The Most From Your Electric Motors,* EASA, 1331 Baur Blvd., St. Louis, MO 63132, (314) 993-2220.

Ebasco Services, *Adjustable Speed Drive Applications Guidebook;* Bonneville Power Administration, 905 N.E. 11th Avenue, Portland, OR, 97232, 1990.

Electric Ideas Clearing House, *Reduction Power Factor Cost;* Bonneville Power Administration, distributed through the Electric Ideas Clearing House, Olympia, (206) 586-6854, 1991.

Electric Ideas Clearing House, *Reducing Power Factor Cost; Optimizing Your Motor Drive System; Buying An Energy-efficient Electric Motor; Energy Management for Industry; North Seattle Community College Two-Speed Motor Case Study*; fact sheets published by the Bonneville Power Administration, distributed through the Electric Ideas Clearinghouse, Olympia, (206) 586-6854, 1992.

Scott Horton, P.E., "Are Energy Efficient Motors a Cure-All for Energy Problems?" *Consulting-Specifying Engineer,* Sept. 1994, pp. 50-54.

Walter Johnson, "Energy Management for Electric Motors; The Benefits of Motor Surveys," *The Demand Side Review Quarterly Magazine,* June 1994, pp.14-19.

Howard Jordan, *Energy Efficient Electric Motors and Their Application;* Van Nostrand Reinhold Co. New York, 1991.

Scott King, *Energy-Efficient Motors: A Study of Their Application in Idaho Municipal Water Supply Systems;* Idaho Department of Water Resources, Boise, 1993.

Robert Lawrie, "Modern Motor Test Techniques", *EC&M;* July 1992, pp.33-46.

Leeson Electric Motors, *Practical Motor Basics;* 1994, Grafton, Wisconsin, 53024.

Rick LeFevre, "Predictive Maintenance Surge Testing", *Plant Engineering;* June 18, 1987, pp. 103-107.

McCoy, Litman & Douglass, *Energy-Efficient Electric Motor Selection Handbook;* 1991, Bonneville Power Administration: P.O. Box 3621, Portland, OR 97208, (document order phone number: (800) 622-4520 or (503) 230-3478).

David Montgomery, "Testing Rewinds to Avoid Motor Efficiency Degradation", *Energy Engineering;* Vol. 86, No. 3, 1989.

David Montgomery, *How to Specify and Evaluate Energy-Efficient Motors;* General Electric Company, Hendersonville, TN.

Nadel, Shepard, Greenberg, Katz & de Almeida, *Energy-Efficient Motor Systems; A Handbook on Technology, Programs and Policy Opportunities;*1991, American Council for an Energy Efficient Economy: 1001 Connecticut Ave. NW #535, Washington, DC 20036, (202) 429-8873; $24.95.

Richard Nailen, "Installing Motors Properly," *Plant Services,* January 1988; reprinted by Lincoln Motors, Cleveland.

Richard Nailen, "A User's View of Motor Repair Standards and Specifications", *IEEE Transactions on Industry Applications;* Vol. 24, No. 6, Nov/Dec. 1988.

Richard Nailen, *The Plant Engineers Guide to Industrial Electric Motors,* Barks Publications, Chicago, 1985.

Richard Nailen, "Nuisance Trips in Motor Circuits: What's the Answer," *Plant Services,* January 1990; reprinted by Lincoln Motors, Cleveland.

Richard Nailen, *Managing Motors: The Complete Book of Electric Motor Application and Maintenance,* Barks Publications, Chicago, 1991.

NEMA MG1-1993; National Electrical Manufacturers Association, 2101 L Street, Washington DC 20037, (202) 457-8400, Fax (202) 457-8411.

Ontario Hydro, *Rewound Motor Efficiency;* Technologic Profile, 1991.

Ontario Hydro, *Motors Reference Guide;* Product Knowledge Reference Guide Series, Technologic Profile, 1990.

Clarence Phipps, *Drive Basics;* Bellevue, 1992.

Power Smart, *Power Factor;* Guides to Energy Management series; BC Hydro, Vancouver, BC, 1990.

Resource Dynamics, *Electric Motors: Markets, Trends, and Applications;* Electric Power Research Institute, 3412 hillview Avenue, Palo Alto, CA 94304, 1992.

Resource Dynamics, *Electric Motor Systems Sourcebook: A Summary of Current Activities: Market Participants; Research & Development; Resource & Tools; Utility DSM Programs; Codes and Standards;* 1993, published by the U.S. Department of Energy, Bonneville Power Administration and EPRI, available from the Motor Challenge Information Clearinghouse, P.O. Box 43171, Olympia, WA 98504-3171, (206) 586-6854.

David Schump, "Motor Insulation Predictive Maintenance Testing," *Plant Engineering;* January 24, 1991, pp. 47-49.

Robert Smeaton, *Motor Applications & Maintenance Handbook;* McGraw-Hill, New York.

John Traister, *Handbook of Polyphase Motors,* Prentice Hall, 1988.

Alan Wallace and René Spée, *High Efficiency Motor Rewind Study;* Bonneville Power Administration, Division of Resource Management, Portland, February, 1991.

Washington State Energy Office, *Industrial Motor Repair in the United States: Current Practices and Opportunities for Improving Energy Efficiency,* Olympia, 1994.

I-iii. SOFTWARE

Allen-Bradley Energy Comparison Software
Description: This software package calculates potential energy savings from using an adjustable speed drive system on pump and fan systems.

Available from:
Allen-Bradley
Drives Division
1201 S. Second Street
Milwaukee, WI 53204
(414) 382-2000

Energy "SAVE" Program

Description: This software package calculates potential energy savings and simple payback from using a Baldor energy efficient motor. This program has default data for situations where users have limited data.

Available from:

Baldor	Baldor, Canadian Distributor
P.O. Box 2400	522 Menton Court
Fort Smith, AR 72902	Mississauga, ON L5R 2Z6
Phone: (501) 646-4711	Phone: (800) 521-4346
Fax: (501) 648-5792	Fax: (315) 253-9923

ASCON I and ASCON II

Description: These Adjustable Speed Drive Analysis (ASCON) Energy Savings and Return on Investment software programs calculate the energy savings from using an ASD on pumps or fans with normal industrial pressures. ASCON I covers by 7.5 to 2,000 horsepower systems, and ASCON II covers larger ones.

Available from:

Power Electronics Application Center
Electric Power Research Institute
10521 Research Drive, #400
Knoxville, TN 37932
Phone: (615) 675-9505

General Electric Energy Savings Analysis

Description: This software package calculates potential energy savings from using an adjustable speed drive system on pump and fan systems. This program has default data for situations where users have limited data.

Available from:

G.E. Drive Products Division
Speed Variation Product Operations
1100 Lawrence Pkwy.
Erie, PA 16531
Phone: (814) 875-2663

MOSCAM

Description: The Motor Speed Control Analysis Model (MOSCAM) software package calculates potential energy savings and simple payback from using an adjustable speed drive system on pump and fan systems.

Available from:
Resource Dynamics Corporation
8605 Westwood Center Drive
Vienna, VA 22182
Phone: (703) 356-1300

MotorMaster

Description: MotorMaster software contains a database with performance and price information on most commercially available three-phase electric motors from 1 to 500 horsepower sold in North America. Data is supplied by manufacturers and updated annually. The program allows users to obtain information, including list price, full and part load efficiency, operating speed, etc. on all motors in a specified horsepower, enclosure, and speed class ranked from highest to lowest full-load efficiency. It also contains analysis features which calculate energy savings and simple payback from an energy efficient motor.

Available from:
Motor Challenge Program
P.O. Box 43171
Olympia, WA 98504-3171
Phone: (800) 862-2086
Fax: (206) 586-8303

I-iv. STANDARDS

NEMA Standards

Price

MG1: Motors and Generators $91
This document provides guidelines and practical information on safety,
testing, construction and operation of electric motors and generators.

MG2: Safety Standard for Construction and Guide for
Selection, Installation and Use of Electric Motors $15
This document sets design standards for specific motor and generator
safety features, their proper selection, installation and use.

MG3: Sound Level Prediction of Rotating Machinery $19
This document provides a method for estimating sound pressure levels of installed motors and generators.

MG7: Motion/Position Control for Motors and Controls $19
This document covers design and power requirements for servo and
stepper motor installation and use.

MG10: Energy Management Guide for Selection and Use
of Polyphase Motors $13
This guide provides information on the proper selection, installation,
operation, and maintenance of polyphase induction and synchronous
motors.

MG13: Frame Assignments for Alternating Current Integral-
Horsepower Induction Motors $10
This standard assists users in selecting the proper frame size, horse-
power and speed when selecting motors for specific applications.

Renewable Parts for Motors $10
This is a reference for the handling of maintenance problems common to motors and generators.

ICS 3.1   Safety Standards for Construction and Guide for
Selection, Installation and Operation of ASD's $19
This document provides recommendations on the proper design, selection, installation, operation and testing of adjustable speed drive systems.

>   *Available from:*
>   National Electrical Manufacturers Association (NEMA)
>   Publications Distribution Center
>   P.O. Box 338
>   Annapolis Junction, MD 20701-0338
>   Phone: (301) 604-8002
>   Fax: (301) 206-9789

Institute of Electrical and Electronics Engineers (IEEE)

112: Standard Test Procedures for Polyphase Induction
Motors and Generators $22.00
This standard defines the proper testing and reporting of induction electric motor and generator performance. It is the basis for most induction motor efficiency testing in North America.

113: Guide to Test Procedures for DC Machines $21.50
This standard defines the proper testing and reporting of direct current electric motor and generator performance.

115: Test Procedures for Synchronous Machines $25.00
This standard defines the proper testing and reporting of synchronous electric motor and generator performance.

428: Definitions and Requirements for Thyristor AC
Power Controllers $23.00
This standard covers thyristor controllers, which are widely used in induction motor systems.

519: Recommended Practices and Requirements for
Harmonic Control in Electric Power Systems $50.00
This document establishes standards for electric power distortion.

739: Recommended Practice for Energy Conservation and
Cost-Effective Planning in Industrial Facilities $31.00
This book provides guidelines for the correct design, operation and
maintenance of industrial and commercial mechanical systems for
cost effective energy conservation and efficiency.

936: Guide for Self-Commutated Converters $31.00
This guide provides definitions, letter symbols, classification, service
conditions, testing, etc. for self-commutated converters.

995: Recommended Practice for Efficiency Determination of
Alternating Current ASDs $36.00
This document describes a method for determining the efficiency of
large, ASD motor systems.

> *Available from:*
> IEEE Customer Service
> 445 Hoes Lane, P.O. Box 1331
> Piscataway, NJ 08855-1331
> Phone: (800) 678-IEEE; (908) 981-1393
> Fax: (908) 981-9667
>
> IEEE Canada
> 7061 Yonge Street
> Thornhill, Ontario L3T 2A6
> Phone: (800) 678-IEEE

National Fire Protection Association (NFPA)

National Electrical Code $32.50
This code covers the proper installation of electrical conductors and equipment, including motors and generators. It is used throughout North America.

70B: Electrical Equipment Maintenance $37.50
This document provides guidelines on basic electric system and equipment maintenance review.

>   *Available from:*
>   National Fire Protection Association (NFPA)
>   Batterymarch Park
>   Quincy, MA 02269
>   Phone: (800) 344-3555; (617) 770-3000
>   Fax: (617) 984-7057

Underwriters Laboratories (UL)

519: Motors, Impedance Protection $20.00
Covers fractional horsepower, permanent-split-capacitor and shaded pole motors.

547: Motors, Thermal Protectors $20.00
Describes the correct the of thermal protection to be used in electric motors.

674: Motors and Generators, for Use in Hazardous $40.00
Locations
Defines specific classes of special motors for use in various flammable and explosive environments.

845: Motors Control Centers $40.00
Covers floor mounted assemblies containing motor control units.

984: Motor-Compressors, Hermetic Refrigerant $30.00
Covers single- and three-phase motors and motor protection systems.

1004: Motors, Electric $30.00

Covers compound series, shunt, and permanent-magnet-field commutator motors.

Available from:
Underwriters Laboratories, Publications
333 Pfingsten Road
Northbrook, IL 60062
Phone: (708) 272-8800

ASHRAE (American Society of Heating, Refrigerating and Air Conditioning Engineers)

ASHRAE/IES 90.1 $98.00

This standard defines minimum efficiencies, sizing and other design guidelines for single- and polyphase induction motors for use in building HVAC systems. Many state and local governments are adopting this standard for their building codes.

Available from:
ASHRAE
1791 Tullie Circle, NE
Atlanta, GA 30329
Phone: (404) 636-8400

Index

A

Acceleration, 54
Affinity Laws, 112
Apparent Power, 68

C

Calculating Energy Costs, 163
Controls, 107

D

Design, 12
Design E , 92
Direct Current (DC) Motors, 7
Duty Cycle, 73
Dynamometer, 28

E

Efficiency, 21
Efficiency Definitions, 31
Efficiency Standards, 87
Efficiency Testing, 26
Electric Ideas Clearinghouse, 202
Electrical Testing, 141
Energy Efficient Motors, 85, 92
Energy Policy Act, 87
Energy Star Building Program, 203
Evaluating Investments, 174, 204

F

Frame Sizes, 13
Frequency, 63

G

Glossary, 217

H

Harmonics, 66
Horsepower, 47

I

Induction Motors, 8
Information Sources, 201
Insulation Testing, 150
Inventory and Test Form, 233
Investment Analysis, 161

L

Load Factor, Determining, 55
Load Factor, 36
Losses, 23
Lubrication, 155

M

Manufacturer Addresses, 192
Mechanical Checkup, 154
Metering Motor Operation, 153
Motor Challenge Program, 92
Motor Circuit Analysis, 144
MotorMaster Software, 194, 199

O

Operating Environment, 80
Organizations, 305
Overheating, 79

P

P/PM, 137, 213
Parts of Motor, 12
Phase Balance, 64
Power Factor, 68
Purchase Specifications, 186

R

Reactive Power, 68
Rebates, 178
Reference Documents, 307
Repair Form, 297
Repair of Motors, 121
Repair Quality Record, 299
Repair Shop Evaluation, 235
Repair Specifications, 257
Replace/Repair Guidelines, 127
Resources, 305
Retail Market, 189
Rewind Guidelines, 132

S

Scheduled Replacement, 158
Selecting Motors, 183
Service Factor, 48
Simple Payback, 175
Single Phase Motors, 7
Slip, 46
Software, 311
Speed, 45
Speed and Load
   Factor Testing, 152
Speed Controls, 11
Squirrel Cage, 10
Staff Training, 213
Standards, 313
Storage and Handling, 157
Synchronous Motors, 7

T

T-frame, 16
Temperature, 76
Testing, 141
Testing Standards, 29
Thermal Testing, 145
Torque, 41
Troubleshooting, 227
Types of Motors, 7

U

U-frame, 16

V

Ventilation and Cleaning, 154
Vibration Testing, 149
Voltage, 59
Wound Rotor Motors, 9